Hard Rock

to

Solid Rock

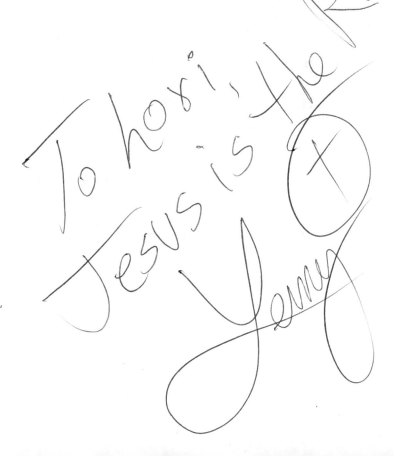

To Lori, the Rock!
Jesus is the X

Jeremy

Published by
Darrell and Lisa Huckaby
2755 Ebenezer Rd. SE
Conyers, GA 30094

Darrell Huckaby
Hard Rock to Solid Rock
Copyright 2002
Printed in the United States of America
First Edition
First Printing

Text Layout Design by Lisa Huckaby
Cover Design by Donald A. Smith—The Adsmith Inc., Athens, GA

ISBN 0-9647867-4-5

Hard Rock
to
Solid Rock

by

Darrell Huckaby

as lived by

Lenny Stadler

Author's Note

This is not a novel, although it is the hope of the author that it will read like one. Neither is it a documentary, although the events depicted in Lenny Stadler's life are true and accurate This is simply the story of one man's life, as best he can recall. That man, Lenny Stadler, has given the author wide latitude in using his creative talents to create specific scenes and particular dialogue that tells Stadler's story in an honest and realistic manner. It is not the intent of Stadler or the author to glorify Stadler's past behavior or disparage any of his contemporaries. It is, however, the intent of both the author and Stadler to testify to the life-changing power and saving grace of Jesus Christ.

Dedicated to

J.W. "Johnny" and Lillie Bullock
Lenny Stadler's maternal grandparents

and

The people of
Julia A. Porter United Methodist Church
Darrell Huckaby's boyhood church home

and in loving memory of
Leonard E. Stadler, Sr.

"For God so loved the world that He gave His only Son. . ."

John 3:16

Prologue

"As the deer pants for the water brooks, so pants my soul for you, O God."

Psalm 42:1

*7*he yellow sports car looked strangely out of place, zooming along the rural back roads near Reidsville, North Carolina. This area, in 1973, was more given to pickup trucks than finely-tuned British convertibles. So, too, did the long-haired young man behind the wheel, not that a passing motorists could have caught more than a glimpse of the desperate person behind the wheel. He was driving much too fast.

They couldn't have seen his eyes at all, as they were hidden behind tinted shades. Anyone who might have looked into those eyes would have found them to be blood-shot—and filled with fear; fear and hopelessness. They were the eyes of a dead man. Spiritually dead, at least. In a few moments, if things went according to plan, the body would join the spirit.

Fear and hopelessness. Fear and hopelessness had been every bit as instrumental as the yellow MGB in bringing Lenny Stadler to this crossroads in his life.

The speedometer needle soared as he drove the car faster and faster. The tires squealed as he pushed the high-performance engine to its very limits. Faster and faster he drove the machine along the blacktop asphalt that he knew by heart.

He drove the car like there was no tomorrow, and if he followed through with his plan there would be none—

literally. Not for him, anyway. Not on this earth. The pain of too many wasted yesterdays and the fear of the unknown made tomorrow too frightening to face.

Pain and fear. Fear and hopelessness. Hopelessness. "Why face tomorrow without hope? Why not end it today?

"Yes," he thought as he gripped the leather covered steering wheel tighter and tighter—pushing the accelerator with even more force. "Why not end it today? Right here. Right now. Death. Death will solve all the problems. When there's nothing to live for, why not choose death? When a life has already been wasted, why prolong it?"

He gunned the engine again, pressing even harder upon the floored accelerator. Just ahead the road would curve sharply. The yellow MGB would not. The end would be swift and painless, at least for the driver.

"I can do it!" he spoke aloud. "I will do it!" he desperately cried, gripping the wheel tighter and trying to push his foot through the very floorboard of his car.

But then Lenny Stadler heard a still, small voice. Above the roar of the engine, the blaring of the radio, and the desperation in his own soul, Lenny Stadler heard that inner voice. A peaceful voice. A voice completely without desperation. A voice that spoke as clearly to Lenny Stadler as if it came from the empty passenger seat beside him.

"I am the way, the truth, and the life."

Over and over that simple statement repeated itself in Lenny's mind.

"I am the way, the truth, and the life."

The voice grew louder and clearer.

"I am the way, the truth, and the life. No one comes to the Father except through me.

"I am the way. I am the way. I am the way."

"Yes," Lenny thought. Another way. Another way. There must be another way. There is another way!"

Lenny Stadler's foot eased off the accelerator of his car. His death grip on the steering wheel loosened. He wasn't aware of it, but tears began to flow from his blood-shot eyes. He steered his car safely through "Deadman's Curve" and brought it to a stop at the first dirt road beyond. And there he sat, his head resting on his car's steering wheel, sobbing—his whole body racked with emotion as a flood of memories washed over him. Precious memories. Memories that had saved his life without his even knowing it. Memories that would form the foundation of a life more rich and full than he could have possibly imagined.

Chapter One

"Then the word of the Lord came to me saying: 'Before I formed you in the womb I knew you; Before you were born I knew you; I ordained you to be a prophet to the nations.'"

Jeremiah 1:4-5

"Lenny, come back here! Where ya goin' in such an all fired hurry, boy?"

The dark haired teenager grabbed two cookies off the plate on the kitchen table, kicking open the screen door and shouting back at his grandfather over his shoulder, "Gotta get home, Pa. Dad will be home for lunch soon."

The older man laughed at his grandson and decided to tease him just a bit. "When have you ever been in a hurry to greet him at the door?"

The teen stopped and smiled. If anyone had been present to witness the short discussion they would have noticed a special affection in the brown eyes of the youngster as he addressed the person he called "Pa."

"Special day, today. Dad promised to bring me a bass today, for my very own."

"A base?" the grandfather asked, feigning ignorance. "Which base? First, second or third?"

Now a big grin split the face of the young teen standing half-in and half-out of the doorway. "You know what I mean, Pa. A bass guitar. I'm getting a bass guitar of my very own today. Dad said so."

"A bass guitar?" Pa asked grumpily. "Why would you want a guitar with just four strings? If you're going to play one of those things, you ought to play one that can hit all the notes. Besides," he added. "If you want to make music, why don't you learn to play the piano, so you can play hymns in church? I never heard anybody play *Amazing Grace* on a bass guitar."

Lenny laughed at his grandfather's comments. "That's Pa," he thought to himself. "Always trying to work the church and the Lord into every conversation."

Out loud he simply said, "Oh, Pa. You know I can't reach the strings on a six-string. It's my hand. It just won't reach around the neck. It's okay though," he quickly added. "I love the bass. I love listening to it. The bass notes in a song just seem to jump out at me. I love the way the bass sounds. I was born to play the bass.

"I'm not playing *Amazing Grace*," though, he added over his shoulder, just before the screen slammed behind him. "I'm gonna play the *Beatles* and the *Rolling Stones.*"

The grandfather chuckled as he walked over to the refrigerator. "That's Lenny," he thought to himself as he reached for the green carton of buttermilk. "Always has to have the last word."

He walked over to the table, and crumpled up two pieces of cornbread, left over from last night's supper, into a tall glass that had once held Welch's grape jelly. As he bowed to give thanks for his lunch and ask forgiveness of his sins he added a postscript—"and Lord, please be with Lenny. Please, Lord. Always be with Lenny."

The minutes seemed like hours to Lenny Stadler as he paced back and forth in his yard. It was a gloriously beautiful day in the North Carolina Piedmont. The sun was shining and there wasn't a single cloud to mar the blue Carolina sky. It could have been twelve degrees and raining alligators and Lenny wouldn't have noticed. The only thing on his mind was the Fender Jazz Bass Guitar that his father had promised to bring home from the music store that day.

Lenny finally grew tired of pacing and sat down on the back steps. His mind wandered. He imagined himself holding the bass guitar he hoped to soon own, remembering how natural it felt in his hands when he had played it in his father's music store. For a while he lost himself in his thoughts, as he pretended to play.

For other boys Lenny's age in Reidsville, North Carolina, the middle years of the 1960s meant three things: football in the fall, basketball in the winter, and baseball in the summer. It was not so for Lenny. Sports held no allure for him and schoolwork was of no importance at all. His true love was music—loud rock-and-roll music—and he spent hours and hours listening to his stereo—picking out the deep, low tones of the bass lines in the compositions and pretending to play along on his own imaginary bass guitar.

He had been trying to teach himself to play the bass while visiting his father at the family-owned music store in downtown Reidsville. The bass felt natural to him. Just like he had told his grandfather earlier in the day, he was made for the bass and the bass was made for him. He had begged and pleaded with his father for months to bring one home from the store so he could begin, in earnest, to master the instrument that felt so comfortable in his hands—and whose sounds felt so natural to his ear.

Finally Lenny had worn his father down—or perhaps the elder Stadler just realized how natural the two—Lenny and the bass guitar—were when put together. At any rate, he had promised that Lenny could have a bass of his very own and the day had arrived for the treasure to be brought home.

As Lenny sat and waited for his dad, his thoughts wandered back to his grandfather. Lenny had never been exceptionally close to his father, but Pa was different. He was a serious, church-going, Bible-reading, God-fearing man and Lenny loved and respected him deeply. But Pa could be too serious sometimes. "It has just been too long since Pa has been young," Lenny often told himself. Pa was always about praying and going to church, and heaven help the fellow who ever got out of line during worship time.

A big grin spread over Lenny's face as he thought about an incident that had occurred five or six years ago. It was homecoming at the old country church that Lenny attended with his parents.

Lenny's parents were once-a-week Christians. They were regular in their Sunday morning attendance and occasionally even made a Wednesday night supper and prayer meeting. But Lenny's grandparents were deeply devoted Christians. They lived for the Lord twenty-four hours a day, seven days a week—and they took it upon themselves to make sure that Lenny was going to be raised in the ways of God.

On the particular Sunday that was playing itself out in Lenny's mind, the pews were filled to the brim for the annual homecoming service. In fact, some of the older members of the congregation were more than a little put out by the fact that they had to squeeze toward the middle of the pews to make room for occasional worshipers who were not regular enough in attendance to realize who sat where on a normal Sunday.

Lenny, who was about eight at the time, was in the balcony—a safe distance from the watchful eye of his grandfather who made it his business, particularly this Sunday, to make sure that his rather restless grandson was in church, sitting up straight, closing his eyes respectfully during prayers, soaking in the scriptures, and getting the full benefit of his time in church—even if he was only eight years old.

On this day, however, owing to the excitement of homecoming, a visiting preacher, and dinner-on the-grounds to follow worship, Lenny had been allowed to sit in the balcony with his cousins, thus making more room for the adults.

Everything would have been fine if the preacher hadn't been so long-winded. He seemed intent on speaking out against every sin mentioned in the Bible and even some that Scripture hadn't thought to mention. An eight-year-old mind can't absorb more than an eight-year-old rear end can endure. Naturally, midway through the sermon, Lenny and his cousins had begun to search for ways to occupy their time—not to mention their wandering minds. The fact that the church windows were open, allowing the sounds—not to mention the smells—of dinner being prepared outside to float in on the gentle autumn breeze didn't help matters.

For a while the youngsters took turns judging bald spots on the more elderly worshippers below. Many of the flock being considerably along in years, the mischievous boys couldn't help but notice that more of the men lacked hair than had hair. Even at their tender ages, they realized that while all men may be created equal, there's a lot of discrepancy among heads. When they tired of this activity, they had begun to fold their worship bulletins into paper airplanes. Over and over they folded and refolded, comparing styles and silently judging the aerodynamics and flight potential of their creations.

Lenny, still sitting alone on his back steps, smiled as he remembered the incident. He really couldn't imagine what had possessed him to launch his paper bomber. What he could remember was the incredible way the wind currents, wafting in through the open windows, picked up his bulletin-turned-dive-bomber. It seemed to hang in the air for an eternity, dipping and diving, rising and falling.

Lenny could still see the face of the visiting preacher in his mind's eye. He had finally reached the climax of his message and was looking toward the heavens, as if for inspiration—ready to drive home his final point. The pastor, a veteran of many, many Sunday morning sermons, could not believe his eyes as he caught sight of a paper airplane making its final approach—right toward his pulpit! A laser guidance system, had one existed in 1960, could not have produced a more direct hit. The youngsters in the church balcony couldn't believe their eyes either, as they watched with mouths wide open and their faces frozen in horror.

The preacher stopped in mid-sentence and watched the invading aircraft crash-land on the podium in front of him. The shocked congregation let out a gasp—unsure whether it was acceptable to laugh out loud in church. All of the congregation except one, that is.

Pa's head turned like it was on a swivel, his eyes honing in on his grandson as if guided by the same laser that might have guided his grandson's aircraft. Lenny would never forget that look. Nor would he forget the whipping his own father administered to him when he got home.

Lenny's father believed in the whole Bible, including the part that said, "Spare the rod and spoil the child." He also tempered justice with mercy, however, and did wait until Lenny had eaten his fill of the incredible meal that always accompanies homecoming preaching at churches throughout the small-town South.

Lenny found himself laughing out loud at the memory.

"Well," said a gruff voice above him. "Are you going to sit there on the steps, laughing the rest of the day, or are you going to play this bass guitar?"

Lost in his reverie, Lenny hadn't even heard a car in the driveway. He looked up with surprise and there stood his father. In his outstretched hand was a candy apple red Fender Bass Guitar.

For several moments Lenny just sat and stared.

"Well," his father repeated. "If you don't want it, I can take it back to the store and sell it to someone who does."

"Oh, Dad!" Lenny exclaimed. "I want it! Boy oh boy, do I want it!"

The youngster jumped to his feet and took the guitar from his dad. He couldn't believe the way it looked and the way it felt in his hands. It was a used guitar, but it didn't matter in the least to Lenny. It was a Fender Bass and it was his.

"Thanks, Dad! Thanks, a lot!" he remembered to shout over his shoulder as he raced inside the house, eager to hook the guitar up to an old, worn-out Fender amp that couldn't possibly handle the lower tones the guitar was capable of producing, but which might not blow completely if the young musician held the volume down.

Lenny Stadler stayed in his room for hours that Saturday, consumed with trying to learn to play the instrument he knew he was created to play. He put his favorite records on his turntable and tried to play along with the bass notes. Late into the morning he played the Fender, long after the rest of his family had retired for the night. It wouldn't be the last time that Lenny Stadler would stay awake most of the night, making music on a bass guitar. Not by a long shot.

Across town, unbeknownst to Lenny, his grandfather was on his knees, saying his nightly prayers—communing with the God that ruled his life. A big part of his prayer that night was devoted to asking God to look over his impetuous thirteen year old grandson, Lenny. It wouldn't be the last time he stayed on his knees, late into the night, praying for Lenny Stadler. Not by a long shot.

Chapter Two

"If we say that we have fellowship with Him, and walk in darkness, we lie and do not practice the truth."

1 John 1:6

"*A*re you sure we're doing the right thing, Leonard?" This question came from Lenny Stadler's mother and was addressed to her husband, Lenny's father, who was already dressed for church and trying to enjoy the Sunday morning newspaper, along with his second cup of coffee.

"Well of course we are," he replied nonchalantly. "Everybody should get up and go to church on Sunday morning. It's the good, Christian, American thing to do." The corners of his mouth turned up in a slight grin, safely behind the paper, of course, and out of his wife's view.

"You know what I mean," she replied, not allowing the tone of her voice to reveal the exasperation she was feeling. "For goodness sakes," she continued. "Lenny is only seventeen years old and there he is, out until all hours of the night, playing that bass guitar. He comes home reeking of smoke. All those other people are so much older than him and who knows what they'll have him getting into. If something were to happen to him I'd never forgive myself."

"Whoa," Lenny's father replied. "Slow down. Take a breath. Relax. We've talked about this before. Lenny is making music—that's all. Along with a little money, of course. He may only be seventeen, but he is good at what he does. And he comes by it naturally. You play the piano and I—well, I play anything with strings. He has a gift. It's almost like he was born to play that bass guitar."

Leonard was on a bit of a roll, himself, now, and didn't intend to slow down until he had made his point. "Those guys Lenny is playing with are good guys. You shouldn't judge them because they like to play rock-and-roll music. What is it they tell us at church? 'Judge not lest ye be so judged?' Don't forget that I make a living selling instruments. Most of those guys bought the guitars and drums they play right there in my store.

"I don't like it when Lenny comes home smelling like smoke, but he's not smoking himself. People probably step outside and take a drink at those places, too—but that doesn't mean Lenny is drinking. He's a good boy and we need to trust him. He won't be able to play his music forever, so I say let him have at it for now."

Dorothy Stadler smiled at her husband. "Well," she said, "He does seem to love playing that bass guitar. I've never seen anything get under his skin like that does. I hear him at all hours of the night plucking away at that thing. And we did tell him he could play out in public as long as his grades didn't suffer."

"And we also told him he could stay out late making music on Saturday night as long as he was up in time for church on Sunday morning," Leonard said, wiping his face with a paper napkin and pushing himself up from the table.

"Lenny," he cried, making his way back to his son's room. "Get up, boy! You're going to be late for church!"

Lenny heard his father's booming voice all the way down the hall, but tried to pretend not to as he squeezed his eyes tightly shut to protect them from the harshness of the light that he knew was about to flood his bedroom.

"Rise and shine!" his father demanded, as he flipped on the light switch and then, adding insult to injury, threw open the curtains that had been purposefully drawn tight against the morning sun. "Get up, Lenny. We need to be leaving the house right now."

The slender, dark-haired teen rolled over in bed and opened one eye, squinting to avoid the harsh light. "Dad," he pleaded, "Can't I sleep in just this once. There was a big crowd last night and we played an extra set. Then it rained all the way from Greensboro so we had to drive real slow. The guys didn't drop me off until nearly 4 a.m."

"I don't care if they didn't drop you off until four minutes ago," his father replied, matter-of-factly. "It's Sunday morning and it's time for church and you're going. If you're worried about your beauty sleep, stay home next weekend. It won't be a problem at all. We're leaving in five minutes. Better get moving."

These last two sentences were uttered over the elder Stadler's shoulder as he left the room. Lenny knew that the debate was over. His head felt like the entire Chinese army had bivouacked inside it the night before and his mouth tasted like they had made it their latrine. He cursed under his breath as his feet hit the floor, resentful that he had to get dressed and spend two hours cooped up inside the Methodist church his family attended, listening to the same old stuff he had heard every Sunday for as long as he could remember.

What he wanted to do was sleep—all day long. Well, maybe, he thought to himself, he could stand a little food in there somewhere, but what he really wanted to do was sleep all day and then go somewhere else and play music all night.

"What a rush," he reflected as he hurriedly used the bathroom, brushed his teeth, and threw water on his face. "Jammin' at a real college fraternity party. And those guys really liked my music. I know they did. It was so cool! And the girls. College girls. Man were they hot! I bet they didn't know I was just seventeen, either," he allowed himself to believe. "If they did, it might not have mattered. Those chicks dig musicians. I could tell."

"Lenny, we're leaving! Let's go."

That was his dad's "I mean business" voice, and it brought Lenny back to reality immediately. "Coming, Dad!" he shouted, throwing on a shirt and pants and sliding his feet into a pair of penny loafers, all at the same time. He grabbed a piece of bacon and a biscuit from the stove as he rushed through the kitchen, wishing he had time to pour himself a glass of orange juice, but knowing better than to risk it.

Lenny hit the back door just as his father impatiently blew his car horn. The car was, in fact, already in gear and moving as he climbed into the back seat. His mother turned and looked at him over her shoulder, frowning disapprovingly at how long her son's dark hair was getting.

"Did you bring your Bible?" she asked.

"No," he replied, trying not to sound too testy. "I don't need it."

"Why don't you need it?" she quizzed him. "Don't you study the Bible in Sunday School?"

"They have them in the room," Lenny answered. "None of the kids bring their own from home. Besides," he teased, "The way Pa quotes scripture every time I'm around him, I just about know the whole thing by heart, now."

"That will be the day," his father said, looking at his son in the rear view mirror as he drove through the streets of Reidsville. "I can see it now. Lenny Stadler, quoting scripture from memory."

Lenny was thankful that the drive to church was short. It made him uncomfortable to be with his parents and talking about scripture so soon after the night he had spent in Greensboro. He had been surprised when his parents agreed to let him play weekend gigs with a local band who needed a good bass player. He knew for a fact that they would not allow him to continue if they knew what really went on at some of the places he played. He was certainly getting an education, an education very unlike the one he received at Reidsville High School. There was beer and wine and whiskey—all for the taking. It was offered to him on a regular basis. His age really didn't matter.

So far he hadn't yielded to the temptation, other than taking an occasional drag from a coed's cigarette or a small sip of beer that tasted like it should be poured back into the horse. Several times his mother had commented about his clothes smelling of cigarette smoke. He knew that she would be shocked if she knew what else was being smoked at some of the places her son was playing.

"Well, are you going in, or are you going to just sit in the car all day?" asked his father.

Lost, again, in his thoughts, Lenny had just about dozed off in the back seat of the car. His father's caustic tone once again stirred him to action and he climbed out of his family's car and headed toward the youth Sunday school department, in the basement of the church.

Lenny didn't really mind Sunday school. In fact, he used to look forward to going, because it gave him a chance to be around his friends—some of whom were girls, and girls had been high on Lenny Stadler's list of priorities for quite some time. And besides, he really did believe the things his teachers told him about God and Jesus and all of that. After all, he had always reasoned, Pa puts a lot of weight in what the Bible has to say. Lenny had only been half teasing when he had said he probably knew much of the Bible by heart. Between his grandfather and his Sunday school teachers, Lenny was probably about as well versed in scripture as most high school students in rural North Carolina.

He listened and accepted what his elders told him about being a Christian without question, and without much of his own thought given to the matter. It was just understood in the Stadler household that you went to church on Sunday, said a blessing before you ate supper, didn't take the Lord's name in vain, and believed what was in the Bible. That was pretty much the extent of his parents' Christianity.

His grandfather, however, was a whole different kind of Christian. Pa was a Scripture reciting, Bible reading, praying-out-loud kind of Christian. He never let Lenny visit him without quoting passages to him and reminding Lenny that he was praying for him daily. As a result of these assurances, Lenny found his visits to his grandfather's house growing more and more infrequent.

There were a lot of cars in the church parking lot, but few people, which meant that the Stadlers were late for Sunday school, which displeased Lenny's father and embarrassed his mother. Lenny didn't care either way, but to keep peace in the family paid attention to his mother's admonition and hurried toward the door.

"Don't forget we're having dinner with your grandparents!" she called to him as he hurried across the parking lot.

"Great," Lenny thought. "More lectures from Pa about the way I look and the music I'm playing." He said nothing, however, and hurried inside.

He smiled at his friends as he entered the classroom and took a seat on the back row. His teacher, a pleasant looking woman in her mid-forties, smiled at the late arriving pupil. Lenny was happy to discover that the lesson was about King David and Bathsheba. The teacher had just asked the class what the word "covet" meant and was waiting for the teens to admit the things in their young lives that had caused them to experience the sin of covetousness.

Lenny didn't offer any comments, but couldn't help but think that he certainly coveted a couple of the college girls that had made eyes at him the night before, in Greensboro. He wasn't sure if any of them were worth sending the guys who had escorted them to the dance to fight in Vietnam, but he certainly could see himself spending an evening in their company.

His thoughts made him laugh out loud, earning him an offer from the teacher to share with the group. He politely declined and tried to pay closer attention to the lesson, which wasn't easy because he happened to have located a seat between the two prettiest girls in class. It was hard to concentrate on David's transgressions when his classmate's *Windsong* perfume was so strongly on his mind.

As the teacher continued with the lesson, Lenny's mind continued to wander, but he was careful not to call further attention to himself. After Sunday school he stopped to talk to some of his other friends from school, wishing more than anything that he didn't have to stay for church, but knowing that skipping was not an option—not if he wanted to retain the freedom of playing music in college towns on Saturday nights. If the previous night was an indication of things to come, Lenny Stadler wanted to spend lots and lots of Saturday nights playing music—and enjoying the perks that came with it.

As it turned out, church was rather painless. Lenny was able to sit in the back with his friends, far from the peering eyes of his parents. Part of the time he spent reliving the previous night and part of the time he sat in a semitrance, eyes open but not seeing—and certainly not hearing--the words of the pastor, who was droning on and on and on, in his usual manner. Lenny's thoughts were far, far away from the banks of the Jordon River, where the preacher's message seemed to originate. His thoughts were in a giant arena in a big city. The house lights were dim and he and an unnamed band were standing in the brightest of spotlights, playing hard rock music, while thousands of fans—mostly female—showered them with cheers and applause after each number.

"One day," Lenny thought to himself. "One day I will be on that big stage."

Before he realized it, the congregation was on its feet, preparing to sing the closing hymn. Lenny hurriedly joined them and began scurrying through his hymnal to find *Have Thine Own Way*, one of three songs the minister usually chose to close his service.

"At least," Lenny thought, "it's not *Just As I Am* again." Then he smiled as he imagined himself returning to his hometown church, having made the big time. He wondered what the older people in the church would think about having one of their own become a big rock-and-roll star. The thought made him so happy that he joined in lustily on the last chorus and sang in a big voice, "*Fill with Thy Spirit, Till all shall see, Christ only, always, Living in me.*"

Chapter Three

*"There is a way that seems right to a man,
but its end is destruction and death."*

Proverbs 14:12

*H*er name was Gail, and she was sixteen. She was also a vision of pure beauty with dark brown hair, expressive brown eyes and a smooth clear olive complexion. Her father used to tease her by saying, "When God made you, he was just showing off." Fathers, of course, are supposed to say things like that, but few who knew this beautiful woman-child would disagree with her dad's assessment.

Certainly not Lenny Stadler. For most of the past four years the two had been a couple—she the vivacious young cheerleader; he the polite young man who preferred playing his bass guitar to playing sports.

Her boyfriend's penchant for rock-and-roll music didn't bother Gail in the least. She liked the new wave of Southern rock herself, and enjoyed hearing Lenny play. She admired the way he could produce sounds from his instrument that few could even imagine, and she loved how his eyes glowed with excitement as they listened to music together as he pointed out the bass lines to her in the songs that came over the car radio.

"Listen to this," he would tell her, over and over. "Listen, now! Here comes the bass. Hear it? Can you hear it? Can you hear the bass cutting in?"

Truth be known, when she first started going out with Lenny Stadler, Gail had barely known one stringed instrument from another. She had listened to the same songs on the radio that everyone else had. She was a huge *Beatles* fan—mostly because she thought George Harrison was so cute—but didn't know, or particularly care, which instrument made which sound.

When she started dating Lenny, though, things changed dramatically. He was all the things she'd ever looked for in a boyfriend. First of all, he was good looking—dark like her, and tall and lanky. Nearly every girl in school thought he was a dream.

But he was also sweet and funny and even-tempered. And he went to church every Sunday, which was a prerequisite for any boy Gail would ever consider dating seriously. It was even more important to her parents, which is why Gail was so uncomfortable as she watched Lenny walk up the steps of her family's home on this otherwise beautiful spring day.

"Hello, beautiful," Lenny walked over to the front porch swing where Gail sat. She was dressed in yellow shorts and a white and yellow striped tank top. Lenny couldn't believe how beautiful she was, and how lucky he was to be able to call her his girl.

Looking around to make sure Gail's parents weren't in sight, Lenny bent over and gave her a kiss. Her lips felt soft and warm as he sat beside her on the front porch swing. Putting his arm around her, he tried to pull her toward him and kiss her again, but he felt her tense under his touch. She pulled her face away from his and uttered those words that every man of every age dreads hearing from his significant other.

"Lenny," she said to him, quietly, yet firmly. "We have to talk."

Confused by the tone of her voice, Lenny tried to dispel the tension by making a joke. "Can't we make-out first and then talk?" he implored with a smile.

"No, Lenny," she replied. "We have to talk now."

At eighteen years of age, Lenny was not an expert on women—or anything else for that matter, but he was smart enough to recognize the combative tone of voice his girlfriend was using. He drew away from her and slid almost imperceptibly across the swing, leaving a few inches of space between them that, symbolically at least, was a chasm.

"Go for it," he told her, all trace of playfulness now gone from his voice as well. "Tell me what we need to talk about that's so important."

Gail thought she had prepared herself for this moment. She had played the scene out in her mind's eye over and over while waiting for Lenny to arrive at her house for their Sunday afternoon date. But now, faced with the actual moment, the words she had so carefully prepared in her mind wouldn't emerge from her lips. Her mouth was dry and she licked her lips a couple of times, preparing to speak, and then losing her nerve.

Sensing that he might grasp the upper hand in whatever discussion was to follow, Lenny regained a bit of his own composure and spoke first, a bit of playfulness returning to his voice. "Well, if you're going to just sit there, I'm going to kiss you some more while you think about what you want to say."

He leaned toward her, but she put her arm against his chest to stop him.

"No," she said, finally finding her voice. "I'm going to say this Lenny, and I'm not going to let you use your charm to keep me from it!"

She took a deep breath, mustering all the courage at her disposal, and blurted out, "Lenny, you either have to give up playing music or you have to give up me!"

The ultimatum didn't really come out like she had practiced it, but she was so glad to have actually gotten the words out of her mouth that she decided to let it stand, without trying to add any further explanation.

Lenny sat for a long while, just looking at the young beauty sitting a few inches from him. He, too, had a hard time finding the right words. Finally he responded with what he knew were the wrong ones.

"Are you crazy?"

"No, Lenny, I'm not," she replied, more sure of herself now. "You are gone every Friday and Saturday night, playing at those clubs and college gigs. I can't date on week nights so about the only time I see you is Sunday afternoon."

She had finally found the courage to speak her mind, and didn't intend to stop until she had said her piece. "We have a really great relationship, don't we?" Sarcasm dripped from every syllable. "We talk on the phone every night. That is, if you're not too busy practicing with one of your bands to call me. On Friday and Saturday nights I sit at home while you are off at who-knows-where doing who-knows-what. Then on Sunday afternoon we go parking for a couple of hours. That's not much of a relationship, Lenny!"

Now Lenny went on the offensive. He didn't even try to keep the anger out of voice. "That's not fair, Gail," he began, "and you know it!"

He stood up to emphasize his point, or maybe because he couldn't stay seated beside someone as beautiful as Gail and remain sufficiently angry to defend his indefensible position.

"You know exactly where I am every weekend and you know exactly what I'm doing! I'm playing music. I'm in a band, Gail. That's what bands do. They play music!"

Aware that Gail's parents might be close by, Lenny sat back down on the swing and lowered his voice. "Look, Gail," he implored. "Be reasonable. I have to play on Friday and Saturday nights. That's when people hire bands. You know that."

"And people play football and basketball on Friday and Saturday nights, too," Gail countered.

"What in the world does that have to do with anything?" Lenny asked.

"Plenty," she replied. Her nervousness was gone and her thoughts were being fueled by an adrenaline rush. "I was a cheerleader, Lenny. Remember? You were jealous.

You could have gone to the games, but you didn't want to. Then you complained about sitting home on Friday and Saturday nights and made me give up cheering. I would have been captain of the squad next year, Lenny. Everybody says so. And I gave it up because you wanted me to."

"That was different," Lenny mumbled.

"How was it different?" Gail demanded.

"It just was. It wasn't just sitting at home. I didn't like going to those games and having all those guys looking at you."

"Oh, get real!" Now it was Gail who was raising her voice. "And I suppose when you go out and play at dances none of those college girls even know you are in the band."

Lenny realized that she was getting the best of this exchange and decided to change tactics. He stood to face her, took her arms in his hands, and looked into her deep brown eyes.

"It's almost summer, Gail." When summer gets here we can see one another during the week. That way the weekends won't seem so bad. Besides. You'll have a car this summer. Maybe your folks will let you come and hear me play."

Gail pulled away from him and sat back down. For the first time during the emotional encounter, a tear rolled down her cheek. She took a deep breath before speaking. All the anger had left her voice, replaced by a sadness that Lenny had never heard and didn't know how to classify.

"My folks don't want me to see you at all this summer, Lenny."

He was dumbfounded. "What do you mean?" he asked. I thought your parents liked me."

"They do like you, Lenny. Or at least they did. They like the old Lenny—the sweet, caring, polite Lenny. They don't like the new Lenny."

"New Lenny?" he responded, truly perplexed. "What do you mean?"

"Look at yourself," Gail told him. "Your hair just keeps getting longer and longer. You only go to church because your daddy makes you. You stay out until all hours playing music."

He tried to speak, but she put up her hand to stop him.

"You are the first person I ever loved, Lenny. But you are changing, and don't even know it. In a few months you will be going off to Elon College. You'll be out playing your bass guitar until all hours at those wild parties. There will be drinking and smoking and worse—and you know it. My parents don't want me involved with someone who is involved with all of that and . . ." Her voice trailed off as she suddenly found the tops of her shoes to be very interesting.

"And what," Lenny challenged.

She looked up into his eyes and with great resolve stated, "And neither do I."

Lenny decided to take one more shot. "You know that having long hair and playing music doesn't mean that

I'm a bad person. I don't have to do all those things just because I play a bass guitar. Playing bass is what I do. Someday I'm going to make it big in music. You'll see. You'll all see. I'm going to be somebody!"

"You already are somebody, Lenny. That's the whole point. Can't you see that?"

Lenny was determined to have the last word. "So you're saying it's music or you?"

Gail sighed, once again, already certain of what Lenny's answer would be. "Yes, she said. "I guess that's what I'm saying."

"Fine," Lenny shouted. "See ya later."

The front door opened and Gail's father peeked out. "Is everything ok?" he asked.

"Yes, Daddy," Gail answered. "Lenny was just leaving."

And Lenny did just that—walking down the steps, getting into his car, and driving away without ever looking back.

Chapter Four

"For as a man thinks in his heart, so is he."

Proverbs 23:7

*L*enny Stadler was a confused young man as he drove away from his now ex-girlfriend's house. On the one hand, he was indignant because she had the nerve to give him an ultimatum about anything—particularly his music. On the other hand, he hated to break up with her because she was a warm and caring person, fun to be with, and—of course—a stunning beauty.

"There are lots of beautiful women, though," he rationalized. "When I get to college in the fall I'll meet hundreds of them. And they will know how to have a good time, too" he continued to reason with himself. "They will appreciate my talents. They'll realize that music makes me somebody!"

Even as he tried to convince himself that he had made the right decision, a part of him knew that Gail had been right about some things. The cheerleading, for one. Lenny had pressured her to quit the squad, even though he knew how much she enjoyed it and even though he knew how popular it helped make her—not that she needed any help in that department.

Lenny wasn't an athlete. He just wasn't interested in football and basketball and baseball. That set him apart from most of the teens in his town. He certainly didn't need his girl hanging out with all the jocks every Friday and Saturday night. "Besides," he lied to himself, "She didn't have to quit. I didn't give her an ultimatum, like she just gave me."

As he continued to drive, not knowing where exactly he was headed, his thoughts turned to other comments Gail had made. He reached up and changed the angle of his rear view mirror, so that he could study his reflection in general and his hair in particular.

"My hair's not that long," he thought to himself. "Not compared to some of the other guys I see when we go to Greensboro to play."

Reidsville, North Carolina was in the heart of the Bible Belt and a very typical and, thus, very conservative, small Southern town. The cultural revolution that began sweeping the country along with the arrival of the boys from Liverpool, several years earlier, was just arriving in the small-town South.

Lenny's mother was reasonably understanding, and hadn't said too much when her son's hair had grown slightly over his ears and began curling up around his shirt collar. She was much more concerned with her son's grades, which had always been adequate, and his behavior, which had never given her cause for alarm. She didn't really approve of her son's new look, but didn't dislike it enough to make an issue of it. More important, to Dorothy Stadler, was the fact that Lenny would graduate and be able to go to a good college in the fall. She was satisfied with the choice Lenny had made and looked forward to having her son enroll in

Elon—just down the road, near Burlington.

His father, on the other hand, understood the music scene, but was more troubled than he cared to admit about his son's appearance. He also didn't like the fact that Lenny came home from his gigs reeking of cigarette smoke. Leonard Stadler believed his son when he told him that he wasn't drinking or smoking or partaking of any of the vices available to a good-looking musician at a college frat party. He was also worldly enough to understand, however, that if you lie down with enough dogs you will eventually wake up with fleas. He was concerned about the changes he had perceived in his son, but didn't want to make an issue of them for fear of driving him further away.

Lenny's grandfather was a different story altogether. He made no bones about the fact that he didn't appreciate the way Lenny looked or acted. Pa was a straight-talking "deep water" Baptist who believed in calling a spade a spade. He fully believed that his grandson was starting down a path that would take him places he shouldn't go—and told Lenny so, every chance he got.

Lenny's thoughts on this Sunday afternoon were not of his parents or grandparents. He didn't even spend an inordinate amount of time focusing on his argument and apparent breakup with Gail. He dismissed her from his mind as soon as he left her driveway and began to think about the coming summer and the subsequent fall, when he would be leaving home and heading off to Elon College.

Elon was a small liberal arts college founded by the

Church of Christ, which pleased his mother and grandparents. It was also within shouting distance of three larger universities—North Carolina State, Duke, and the University of North Carolina in Chapel Hill, which pleased Lenny. He knew that he could find anything he was looking for at those schools. What he would be looking for most was a chance to have fun, meet women, and play his bass guitar—not necessarily in that order.

Play the bass. That brought a smile to Lenny's lips. That would be his ticket to the big time. That would bring him stardom. He had no doubt that he would one day play under the bright lights in the big arenas, and didn't care who he had to step on or over to realize his dream.

Lenny looked down at his dashboard clock and was surprised to see that he had driven around Reidsville, lost in his thoughts, for almost an hour. With great irritation he realized that he had promised his mother that he would bring Gail by the weekly gathering of the clan at his grandparents' house. That was the last place he wanted to go on this Sunday afternoon, especially since he would have to explain why Gail wasn't with him.

"Oh, well," he reasoned, "I'll think of something to tell them about Gail, and pretty soon I'll be on my way, and I won't have to worry about what anyone says." He had actually talked himself into a pretty good mood by the time he arrived at his grandparents' house. That good mood disappeared as soon as he walked through the back door and into the kitchen where his family was gathered.

"The barber shop in town close down, boy?" his grandfather asked, with a scowl on his face.

"I don't want to hear that, Pa." Lenny sounded a bit more testy than he had intended. He loved his grandfather deeply, but was in no mood to listen to his nagging, which seemed to get more and more frequent each week.

"Lenny," his mother scolded. "Don't speak to your grandfather in that tone of voice!"

Knowing he had crossed the line, Lenny quickly grew quiet. Pa, however, had not finished having his say. "Lenny, I'm worried about you. You're changing a little bit and it isn't for the better. I want you to know that I'm praying for you. Now I've prayed for you all your life, but now I'm praying just a little bit harder."

Now Lenny was really embarrassed and wished he were anywhere but in his grandparents' kitchen, being dressed down in front of his entire family, but he had spoken out of turn once, which only added fuel to his grandfather's fire. He wasn't about to talk back again. Instead he simply said, "Okay, Pa" and tried his best to blend into the scenery. As soon as he could do so without drawing too much attention to himself, he said his goodbyes and eased out the back door.

To his dismay, his grandfather followed him out to his car. The old man and the young man stood face to face. Lenny was surprised when he realized for the first time that he was taller than Pa and had to look down to meet his gaze. He couldn't help but remember all the times their positions had been reversed over the past seventeen years and it was he looking upward into those same eyes he now dreaded seeing.

"Lenny," his grandpa stated," You'll be away from home and on your own in just a couple of months."

"It won't be soon enough," Lenny thought to himself.

"Yes, sir, Pa. I know," was all he said.

"It's a rough world out there," his grandfather continued. "There's lots of meanness; lots of temptation; lots of bad things to get into. You've been raised right, Lenny, but I'm afraid you're beginning to wander away from your raising."

Lenny tried to reason with his grandfather. "Pa," he started, "just because my hair is getting a little longer and I like to play rock-and-roll music doesn't mean I've turned into a different person."

His grandfather held up his hand to stop him. "I'm not talking about your hair now," he said with conviction. "I'm talking about your heart. You just watch that you don't throw in with a crowd that will lead you down the wrong road."

"Pa," Lenny replied, again a bit too testily, "there is just no cause for you to worry about me."

"But I am worried about you," was the solemn reply. "And I'm praying for you. I want you to know that. I'm praying for you and I aim to keep praying for you."

With that he turned and made his way back into the

house, leaving Lenny to sit in his car and contemplate why in the world this man who had meant so much to his life was so concerned over his hairstyle and his music. When he finally cranked his car and drove away, he still didn't fully understand what had transpired.

If he could have seen the future he would have turned right around and driven back to his grandfather's welcoming embrace. But that would have been too easy.

Chapter Five

"For all have sinned and fallen short of the glory of God."

Romans 3:23

*I*t was a beautiful day on the campus of Elon College. The sun was shining, the temperature was hovering in the low eighties, and the sky was a beautiful shade of Carolina blue. There were students everywhere. Some were sitting on beach towels and blankets with text books sprawled all around, trying mightily to keep their thoughts on such dreary subjects as Foust and Milton and analytical statistics while their minds were already on spring break, which was still a couple of weeks away. A touch football game was about to begin on the wide green lawn in front of the student union. In short, it was just another typical day in paradise.

Two girls in cut-off jeans and T-shirts were self-consciously tossing a Frisbee back and forth near the edge of the lawn. They couldn't make up their minds if they were more afraid that the male students playing football would notice their awkward throws or that they wouldn't notice them at all. A sudden gust of wind caught the yellow plastic disc and carried it far over the head of its intended recipient, who laughingly chased it toward its final resting place, at the base of a large oak tree.

Sitting at the base of the tree was a long-haired young man wearing bell-bottomed jeans, a long sleeved paisley shirt, and leather sandals. The young man was apparently a student, because an anatomy book and spiral notebook lay beside him on the grass, but his long hair and droopy mustache made him look strangely out of place among the clean-cut and active college students that surrounded him.

As the coed approached him, he carelessly leaned over and picked up the errant Frisbee. A smile of recognition crossed his face as he offered the recovered toy to his owner.

"Hello, Beth. Did you lose this?" he said to the confused young lady who had slowed down as she approached the tree and the young hippie sitting under it.

"Do I know you?" she asked, trying desperately to recognize the person behind the Fu Man Chu and shoulder length hair.

"You should," was the reply. "I was just a year behind you at Reidsville High."

"Lenny!" she blurted out, recognizing the speaker's voice and the brown eyes at the same time. Laughing nervously she added, "I'm sorry. I didn't recognize you. I heard you were at school here and I wondered why I never saw you."

Lenny laughed at this remark and stood up. "Maybe we just don't hang out at the same places," he offered, adding, "Where do you spend most of your time?"

"At the Baptist Student Union," the girl named Beth replied, quickly sorting through her memory bank and cataloging everything she knew—or thought she knew—about her former school-mate. "You're Methodist, aren't you?"

she asked, in an effort to find common ground for a conversation.

Lenny laughed at this remark. "I'm a bass player," he answered. "I put together my own group, along with some guys on my hall. We're playing tonight over in Chapel Hill. It's for a hump-day party at some fraternity. Why don't you come?"

Beth wasn't sure if the invitation was sincere or not and, in fact, wasn't sure if she wanted it to be or not. Normally she wouldn't look twice at one of the campus radicals, which she assumed her former acquaintance had become, especially since he was a freshman and she an upper classman, but she felt an inexplicable attraction for the long haired young man standing before her, nervously tapping her rescued Frisbee against his leg.

She was surprised to hear herself asking, "If I say yes will you give me my Frisbee back?"

"I might," Lenny answered, admiring Beth's beauty and her long dark hair.

"Well, I need to study," she began to hedge, "but I guess I could drive over for a little while. Can I bring a friend?" she asked, indicating the tall blonde beauty who had grown tired of waiting for her friend to return to their game of catch and was now approaching the duo under the oak tree.

"Oh yes," Lenny replied. "You can bring anybody you want. Just tell them you're with the band."

"Gloria, this is Lenny Stadler," Beth said to her friend.

"We're going to hear him play music tonight."

"Hello, Lenny," the blonde said, and then to her friend, "Where? What kind of music?"

Beth smiled flirtatiously at Lenny. "Where?" she parroted. "What kind of music?"

Lenny returned her smile. "At the Kappa Alpha house on the UNC campus," he offered, and then added smugly, "And there is only one kind of music."

"Oh, really now," Beth chided him. "And what kind of music might that be?"

"Rock," he replied. "Hard Southern rock."

"Well," Beth said, "We might come hear you."

She took her friend by the arm and they began to jog away. Beth shouted back at Lenny teasingly over her shoulder, "Then again, we might not."

Lenny smiled as he watched the two girls running across the lawn. "They'll be there," he said to himself. He thought about returning to his perch under the tree but thought better of it. Gathering up the text book that he was yet to open, he headed, instead, back to his dorm room to get ready for a night that was growing more promising by the minute.

Neither of the two girls who nervously emerged from the beige Ford LTD parked haphazardly alongside the curb near the UNC KA house had ever been to a fraternity beer bash. In fact, both had survived two very sheltered years at Elon College without so much as tasting beer or smoking a cigarette. They felt a bit guilty as they approached the large white house with a giant Confederate flag hanging from the front porch balcony.

Both girls were dressed in preppy button-down oxford shirts. Beth's a-line skirt was of brushed denim, Gloria's of khaki. Both girls had cardigan sweaters thrown over their shoulders and tied around their necks. Expensive gold jewelry completed their ensembles and they looked just like every other girl spilling out of the party and onto the KA lawn.

Even before they reached the front porch they could hear loud rock-and-roll music coming from inside the house. A friendly-looking red-haired boy in khaki pants and a blue polo shirt handed Beth and Gloria foaming cups of draft beer as soon as they stepped inside the door. They looked at one another for support, neither really wanting the beer, but not knowing how to go about declining it, either.

Beth immediately wished she hadn't come. She looked nervously around the room, which was packed with young men and women, some of whom were dancing but most of whom were standing in small groups drinking beer and talking. Almost all had cigarettes in their hands. She turned to her friend and shouted over the din of the party, "Are you absolutely certain that we want to stay here?"

Gloria wasn't any more comfortable than Beth, but was actually curious to experience the party, for better or worse. "Let's stay a little while," she said to her friend, and timidly took a sip from the foaming cup of beer she held in her hand. "Ooh," she complained, making a face and wrinkling up her nose. "It's disgusting." She took another sip and, taking the initiative, said to Beth, "Let's go up close to the band and try to get your friend's attention."

They pushed through the crowd, trying to avoid being burned by glowing cigarettes or sloshing beer on themselves, until, finally, they found themselves in front of the makeshift stage where Lenny's band was pouring themselves into their music—mind, body, and soul.

Beth found herself staring at Lenny Stadler. She still found it hard to believe that the wild-eyed bass player was the mild mannered young man she remembered from Reidsville High. She kept moving around, trying to place herself in his line of sight and catch his eye. She noticed that Gloria was paying much more attention to the drummer—who looked like he might have been a few years older than the other three members of the combo.

Lenny finally looked up from his music-induced reverie and as his eyes caught those of Beth he smiled, or actually smirked, as if to say, "I knew you would show up."

In spite of herself, Beth found herself mesmerized by the beat of the music and the gyrations's of the band's bass guitarist. She had never really paid much attention to rock musicians and was surprised—perhaps shocked would be a better word—at the amount of passion Lenny Stadler was pouring into his performance. She began to move almost involuntarily with the deep sounds emitting from his instrument and without even realizing it began to drink the beer she held in her hand. To her utter surprise, when another polo-shirt-clad fraternity man came up and offered her another, she readily accepted it, as did Gloria, who was enjoying herself as much as Beth.

When the set ended, Lenny, who was sweating profusely, grabbed the other members of the band and brought them down front to meet his friends. Sensing an attraction from the overly friendly reaction to the introductions, the band's drummer stayed around after the other two members of the group said hello and moved off toward the beer kegs in the back of the house.

Lenny took Beth's beer from her hand and took a long swig, wiping the foam from his mouth with the back of his hand. "Well," he asked, "What did you think?"

"Y'all were great," Beth answered. "You're not done yet, are you?" she continued.

Lenny smiled at her enthusiasm. "No," he replied. "We have one more set. We just needed to mellow-out first. You play as hard as we do and you might just burst into a ball of flame if you're not careful."

Beth had no idea what he had meant by that statement, but Lenny apparently found himself very clever because he laughed out loud at his own remarks. "Come on," he said, to the other three. "Let's go out back and get some fresh air. Or something," he added with a grin.

Both Beth and Gloria were surprised to find that their legs just didn't work like they usually did as they started to follow the boys in the band through the darkened room.

Beth grabbed Lenny's arm for stability and he responded by putting his arm around her waist and leading her out a side door onto a small covered portico.

"It feels good out here," Beth remarked, looking over her shoulder at Gloria who, to Beth's amazement, had her arms wrapped around the shoulders of the drummer she'd just met five minutes earlier. Their lips were locked in deep kiss.

When she turned back to Lenny, she was even more amazed to see that he was lighting a cigarette with a Bic lighter. It wasn't a normal cigarette, though. It looked home-made, like the ones her grandfather used to make out of white paper and Prince Albert tobacco. But Lenny's was shorter and fatter than her grandfather's and Beth knew immediately that she was, for the very first time, watching someone fire up a joint.

She could feel her heart pounding in her chest as she watched Lenny put the marijuana cigarette to his lips and inhale deeply. He held his breath for a few moments, trying to get the full effect of the drug, then offered it to Beth. She noticed that her hands were shaking and her palms were wet with sweat as she reached up to take it from him. Then she came to her senses and realized where she was and who she was.

She pulled her hand back quickly, as if she had touched a hot stove. "Lenny," she almost shouted. "Are you crazy?"

Beth looked guiltily at the empty cup in her hand

and then turned and grabbed her friend Gloria, pulling her forcibly out of the embrace of a person whose name she barely knew. "Come on," she insisted over her friend's protests. "We've got to go."

She didn't even speak to Lenny as she pushed past him and back into the frat house, looking in every direction for the front door.

Lenny just laughed. "More for us," he said to his drummer. "Have a toke."

The two musicians laughed like that was the funniest statement anyone had ever made and took turns taking deep drags on their joint, getting ready to go back inside the party and make raucous music.

Chapter Six

"Do not forsake your own friend."

Proverbs 27:10

"You're a jerk, Stadler! A real jerk!" The charge was being leveled on a Thursday night by an angry young guitarist that had just learned that his group's bass player was leaving the band high and dry with two weekend gigs coming up.

"Yeah, Lenny," chimed in a second member of the band. "You are a jerk! A real jerk! I mean big time!"

The object of the anger, Lenny Stadler, reclined on his bunk in the tiny college dorm room he shared with an English major from Pennsylvania who, thankfully, was seldom around. Typically laid back anyway, Lenny was even more so now, thanks to the two joints he had smoked before calling his so-called friends to break the news that he wouldn't be joining them for their two weekend engagements—one at an NC State fraternity party and the other a teen nightclub in Durham.

Lenny had found bigger fish to fry, or so he thought. He had been offered to play with a group that had a standing gig in a nightclub near Greensboro, two nights a week. The work was steady and, more important to Lenny, at the Greensboro location there was a much greater chance of hooking up with an even better band for even bigger gigs.

That was all that mattered to Lenny Stadler, who hardly resembled the person who had left Reidsville scarcely nine months earlier. That Lenny Stadler would have felt a sense of loyalty to his friends. He would never have considered standing up his group the night before a booking. Of course, that Lenny Stadler would not have been involved in the booze and drugs that this Lenny Stadler was dabbling in, either. There had been lots of changes in Lenny Stadler since he arrived at Elon College—none of them for the good.

Finally, he decided he needed to respond to the verbal attacks and answered, "I'm a jerk?" Then he laughed. "I may be, but at least I'm good. Way too good to keep playing at nickel-and-dime joints like you guys play. That's why I got invited to play in Greensboro and y'all didn't."

"Nickel-and-dime joints!" The guitarist was incensed and his friend had to grab him to keep him from charging the laconic figure on the bed. "You were sure glad to get this gig four weeks ago, when we agreed to do it! You weren't such a big shot then!"

"Well, that was three weeks ago. This is now. Besides," Lenny added. "You didn't seem so concerned when you took me away from my last band to come play with you. If I remember correctly, you called on a Saturday afternoon to have me play with you Saturday night. You gave me an extra fifty bucks to break off with them and help you out that night.

"Not only that," Lenny reminded them, "I was the one who helped you score some good weed that night and I'm the one the chicks came up to after we were done with the gig. You're just mad because now you'll have to find your own Mary Jane and your own poon tang."

Lenny laughed at his own clever alliteration.

"Let's go," the peacemaker of the group said to the guitarist. "That scum's not worth getting all bent out of shape over. He's all about Lenny. He was never about our group anyway."

"Don't let the door hit you on the way out," Lenny called after them.

After the confrontation was over, he swung his long legs over the edge of the bed and sat up, trying to remember what it was that he was getting up to do. "Oh yeah," he thought to himself. "I was going to light up another joint and get mellowed out."

He sat on the side of the bed for an indeterminable amount of time. In his mind it could have been two minutes or two hours. As he sat there he had a conversation with himself. "They don't know the half of it," he said aloud. "I don't care what I have to do or who I have to step on or step over. I'm going to make it. I'm going to be a big star. I'm going to be the best bass player with the best band in the history of rock-and-roll. I'm going to the big time, even if I have to sell my soul to get there."

Finally he stood up and walked over to the metal dresser he shared with his roomy. He dug around under his T-shirts and socks, cursing to himself under his breath when he realized that he had depleted his stash of marijuana cigarettes. Then he smiled as he realized that in a couple of hours he would be in Greensboro with his new band, playing hard rock music—and wherever hard rock music was played—marijuana was plentiful.

"Yeah," he told himself. "Marijuana and just about anything else your heart desires."

Lenny reached up and turned on the radio that was on top of the dresser. He expected to hear the music of *Three Dog Night* or *Steppenwolf* or some other popular rock group come blaring out of the stereo speakers. Instead the radio was tuned to an AM gospel station. The station was signing off the air for the day and Perry Como was singing the Lord's Prayer.

Lenny surprised himself by sitting back down on the bed and listening. Halfway through the song he began to feel guilty about listening to a prayer while high on weed. Then the guilt turned to anger and he stormed across the room and snatched the stereo's plug out of the wall outlet in an effort to stop the noxious music.

At that same time, thirty miles away in Reidsville, an old man and old woman were sitting down to a dinner of chicken-and-dumplings and black-eyed peas. The old man, Johnny Bullock, bowed his head and returned thanks over the meal. After thanking the Lord for the bounty of the earth and beseeching Him to forgive him for his sins, he prayed ferverently, "And Lord, please help Lenny. He's lost dear God, I know he is. He has turned his back on his raising and I'm afraid, dear God, that his day will come before he's seen the light. Be with Lenny. Please, God. Help him find the way back to you—while there is still time."

And Johnny's wife, Lillie, added a heartfelt "Amen."

Chapter Seven

"The effectual, fervent prayer of a righteous man avails much."

James 5:16

*L*enny Stadler wasn't a happy camper as he stood in front of the mirror in the communal bathroom in the Elon College dorm, brushing his teeth. He felt, in fact, like he was living in a Charles Dickens novel—he was experiencing the best of times and the worst of times.

On the one hand, he was having a blast. He had joined four different rock groups in the past fifteen months— each better than the other. He was playing his bass guitar all over the North Carolina piedmont. Weekends, week nights, it didn't matter. If people were willing to gather and hear cool music, Lenny and his friends were willing to play it.

He reached up and wiped the fog off the mirror, the better to study his reflection. He liked what he saw. His hair was longer than ever, way past his shoulders. His mustache was long, too—the ends protruding past his chin. He looked tough—like a rebel. "And that's what I am," he thought. "I'm a rebel, and I don't care about anybody or anything."

His appearance caused quite a stir during his recent visit home. He had begun to avoid going home because he didn't like getting hassled by his parents about his appearance and his activities and he especially didn't like getting preached to by his grandfather.

Lenny couldn't avoid going home altogether, of course. His father, after all, owned a music store, which is awfully convenient for a nineteen-year-old college student trying to make his way in the music world. It was usually worth putting up with the biting remarks his father had about his hair and his nocturnal habits to get the equipment his band-of-the-month happened to need at a reasonable price—or, better yet, for free—or at least for a promise to pay.

Lenny's mother was more conciliatory and tried to avoid creating a scene. She was more concerned with the fact that her son didn't seem to have any academic direction. He was barely passing most of his classes and still had no idea what he intended to choose for his major. If Dorothy Stadler had known how infrequently Lenny attended class, she would have been amazed that his grades were as good as they were.

Pa was a different matter altogether. Lenny had gotten to the point of avoiding his grandparents' home altogether, even when he did pay a visit to Reidsville. All Pa wanted to talk to him about was God and sin and the path to hell and the power of redemption. Lenny realized, on some level, that he was hurting both his grandparents by staying away from them, but he couldn't bring himself to care. They just got on his nerves way too bad with all their talk of religion and he felt uncomfortable for days at a time after visiting their home and hearing their sermons.

Lenny couldn't remember the last time he had attended church.

The previous week had been Thanksgiving, though, and there was just no getting around going home for Thanksgiving. It might have been the most miserable afternoon of Lenny Stadler's young life. It rained buckets all day long, trapping Lenny inside the house. He tried in vain to create a reason to go for a drive so he could smoke one of the cigarettes he had stashed in his car's glove compartment or, better yet, one of the joints that was hidden under the driver's seat. He wasn't bold enough to smoke in front of his family, even though they probably suspected he had picked up the habit. After all, anyone who looked as rough as Lenny did would probably do just about anything. "At least," he thought, "that's probably what they think." He hated to admit, even to himself, how close they would have been to the truth if those were his family's thoughts.

The worst part of the day, however, had not been the tension caused among his family by Lenny's radical appearance. His mother, ever the peace keeper in the family, had given strict instructions to all assembled—her husband included—that conversation, or even comments, about Lenny's hair, clothes, mustache, and music were off limits. Lenny knew what they all were thinking, but out of deference to his mother, they said nothing.

Unfortunately, Dorothy Stadler could not boss her own father around, especially not in his own house, and he had plenty to say to and about his grandson from the time Lenny arrived. Lenny tried, at first, to laugh off the comments, but he quickly tired of hearing about how bad he looked and what a big disappointment he had become. He finally spoke sharply to his grandfather, imploring him to leave him alone. "If you don't like how I look, Pa, then why don't you just not look at me!" Lenny had shouted at the old man before storming into the living room and feigning interest in the Dallas Cowboys football game.

The absolute worst part of the day had been at the dinner table, when Johnny Bullock openly asked God to "save Lenny from the path of doom and destruction he has chosen for himself and welcome him back into your fold with open arms."

Absolute silence filled the dining room for several minutes after the prayer as the family members awkwardly passed around huge platters of turkey and dressing and steaming hot vegetables. Eventually conversation resumed, but not for Lenny. He sat and ate in silence, seething with anger at his family with every bite of food.

When the meal had mercifully ended, Lenny excused himself as soon as he possibly could and prepared to leave. As he had so many times before, grandfather followed grandson to the back door, grabbing Lenny's arm and turning him around—forcing the lost young man to look him right in the eye.

"You can hide from yourself, Lenny," Pa said, "but you can't hide from God."

Exasperated, Lenny shot back, "Pa, what in the world do you mean by that? I'm not hiding from anything or anybody. I'm just being myself, and you don't like who I really am."

His grandfather never wavered. "You know that's not true, boy. I want you to know that I get out of bed every morning at 4 a.m., and every morning at 4 a.m. I am on my knees praying—praying for you, Lenny—praying that God will touch your heart—praying that God will wake you up—praying that you'll come to your senses, before it's too late."

"Well do us all a favor, Pa—me, you, and God," Lenny shouted back. "Sleep a little later every morning and just leave me out of your prayers!"

Lenny pulled away from Pa's grasp and ran out into the rain, throwing gravel in every direction as he drove away from his grandparents' house.

And now here he was, three weeks later, staring into a cloudy mirror in a noisy dorm bathroom, reliving each awful moment of that awful day. If that wasn't bad enough, he had an English final in an hour. Before he could go and take the English exam, for which he was not in the least prepared, he had to go by and listen to his advisor tell him how disappointed she was in him because he "wasn't working up to his potential."

No, Lenny Stadler was not a happy camper as he finished brushing his teeth and walked slowly down the hall toward his dorm room.

"Mr. Stadler," the middle-aged lady in the beige business suit was saying to the long haired college student sitting uncomfortably across the desk from her, "You just aren't working up to your potential. We expected much more out of you when you were accepted here at Elon. Do you realize that you are one of the few students in the sophomore class who hasn't even declared a major?

"And your grades," she went on. "I've spoken with your professors and, quite frankly, Mr. Stadler, unless you do exceptionally well on your final exams, I suspect that your GPA will fall below the acceptable level. I'm afraid you might just spend winter quarter on probation."

Lenny sat and stared despondently at the well-meaning lady sitting across from him. He heard what she was saying and her words meant no more to him than if she was telling him that the price of bologna in the Dominican Republic was expected to double by Christmas. As usual, he was simply going through the motions—putting on an elaborate charade. He didn't care about his grades, he didn't care about probation, he certainly didn't care how much he was disappointing the faculty of Elon College.

What he cared about was playing his bass guitar, getting high, and finding female groupies. What he really cared about was finding a group of musicians that were as talented as he was so he could forget about school and small-town gigs and make the big time.

What he said was, "Yes, ma'am. I'm sure I'll start to do better."

He stood to leave, and as he headed for the door, his advisor said to him, "I pray that you do, Mr. Stadler, before it's too late."

Her words rang in his ears as he walked across campus toward the English building. "She's just like Pa," he said to himself. "I pray that you do!" he mocked her in his mind. "Don't people have enough to pray about without praying that I will turn into a boring, intellectual with a short hair cut and a 3.5 GPA?"

Lenny continued to talk to himself as he strode toward his classroom. He became angrier and angrier with every step. He was the last student to arrive in the second-story classroom where his final was being given. The professor had already handed out the tests to the rest of the class and stared disapprovingly at Lenny when he walked through the door.

Lenny self-consciously took his seat and waited for his instructor to chastise him for his tardiness. Instead the teacher simply walked over and placed a copy of the exam on Lenny's desk without making any comment whatsoever. For some reason, this made Lenny even madder than if he had been scolded for coming in late. He opened the test and stared at the first question, which was some sort of essay about Milton's vision of God in *Paradise Lost*.

"God again," Lenny said. He wasn't sure if he had said it aloud, or simply to himself. "Everywhere I look," he thought, "there's God! Everywhere I go, somebody's going to pray for me. God, God, God! I'm sick of hearing about God!"

Lenny took out his pen and wrote on his paper, "I

don't know what Milton thought about God, but my vision of Paradise involves a bass guitar, dark brown haired girls, and that good weed from Bogota."

Lenny's hand started shaking as he scribbled his cryptic message. His breath began to come harder and, to his surprise, his shoulders started shaking and his bottom lip began to quiver. "That's it," he said—this time out loud. "I'm just not playing this stupid game any more!"

"What did you say, Mr. Stadler?" the startled professor asked.

At first Lenny didn't say anything in response. He just sat and stared into space. Finally, he stood up, gathered his belongings, and walked toward the door, tossing his unfinished exam on his teacher's desk. "I said, 'I quit,'" Lenny said as he brushed past his professor and out the door. He then threw his books down the hallway, as he stormed out of the building.

He felt like the weight of the world was off his shoulders as he hurried back to his dorm room, where he packed his belongings, hauled them to the parking lot, and crammed them into the trunk and back seat of his automobile. When he was finally loaded up, he cranked his car and headed it toward Reidsville, never once looking back.

Chapter Eight

*"And not many days after, the younger son . . .
journeyed to a far country, and there wasted his possessions
with prodigal living."*

Luke 15:13

*L*eonard Stadler was working behind the counter of his music store in downtown Reidsville. It was the first week of December and the busiest time of the year. He would sell more beginner's guitars in the next three weeks than the rest of the year put together.

Selling guitars to novice players who may or may not ever learn a single chord was not what he enjoyed most about his business, of course. Leonard Stadler was a craftsman, and he loved building guitars by hand. Just as his son, Lenny, knew that he would one day play bass in a big time rock-and-roll group, Leonard knew that his instruments would one day be in the hands of the country's finest artists.

But selling guitars, picks, strings, and harmonicas, along with sheet music and the like, kept the rent paid and the lights on, and the rush was about to begin. So on this particular December afternoon, Stadler, who knew he couldn't sell what he didn't have in stock, was checking his inventory and making sure it was up to date.

The last person in the world he expected or wanted to see walk through the front door was his son, Lenny. But when the jingle bells attached to the front door chimed and Stadler looked toward the door, it was, indeed, his son Lenny who came walking in.

"Boy, what are you doing here in the middle of the week? I thought your exams weren't over until next Monday." Leonard had been frustrated with his son for the past eighteen months, and his voice had more of an edge than it might have, which immediately put the younger Stadler on the defensive.

"I quit, Dad," he countered. "I quit and I'm not going back. And nothing you can say will make me change my mind."

Leonard came out from behind the counter and took several long strides toward his son. He was a big man, and still cut an intimidating figure, even though Lenny himself was almost six feet tall. "What do you mean, you quit?" was his father's predictable reaction. "You can't just quit school without talking to me and your mother. We've spent a fortune keeping you in that school. You'd better get right back to Burlington and figure out how to fix whatever you've fouled up!"

Leonard Stadler was angry, and wasn't in the least interested in explanations or excuses.

"I'm not going back to school, Dad--ever." Lenny had prepared himself all the way home for what he knew would be an ugly scene. He knew exactly what his father's reaction would be and was determined not to back down. And one thing he knew with absolute certainty. He was not going back to Elon College.

"What in the world do you think you're going to do then? You're certainly not going to freeload off your mother and me. What kind of job do you think you can get? What kind of life do you think you can have without an education?" Leonard was red in the face and almost shouting now. He did, however, have the presence of mind to walk over and lock the front door of his music store and turn the hanging sign around to tell the general public that he was closed—at least for the time being.

"What do you think you can do?" he repeated, "without an education?"

"I can play my bass guitar," Lenny answered. "That's what I'm good at and that's what I like to do. School is just getting in my way. I can't play any gigs except right in this area. I can't get out and get an agent to find me good jobs. I'm ready to move on. I'm going to put together a group that the whole world will want to see. Nothing I'm learning in college will help me do that!"

"Look at you!" his father attacked, totally disregarding everything his son had said. "You look disgusting! You look like a freak, with hair hanging down your back and those stupid clothes you wear. You've turned into a bum. It's not about music. It's about chasing girls and being sorry in general. That's your problem. You've just turned sorry, and I won't stand for it! You're going back to school and you're going back right now!"

Leonard's face was as red as the first guitar he had bought his son, six years earlier, and the veins were bulging in his forehead.

But Lenny stood toe to toe, his voice rising to the

same level of his father's.

"And look at you!" he shouted back. "Fifty years old and standing behind a counter in a little hick town. Is that what you want me to do? Stay here in Reidsville like you? Forget it, Dad! I'm going to live my life the way I want to live it! I don't care what you or anybody else says."

Lenny was livid now. Stung by his father's criticism, he was determined to strike back. He wanted to hurt his father as much as his father had hurt him. For fifteen minutes the argument raged, father and son screaming at one another, each exchange becoming more and more vicious. At one point Lenny believed that his father would strike him, and if he had stayed much longer, they might have come to blows.

Instead, Lenny pointed his finger right in his father's face—the only time in his entire life he would do so—and said through clinched teeth, "You are not going to tell me how to live my life. Do you understand me? You are not going to tell me how to live my life. I'm going to live my life my way!"

With that, he stormed out of the music store, slamming the door behind him so hard that the plate glass nearly shattered. He never looked back. Just like when he left Gail's house on that fine spring day. Just like when he left his grandfather's house on Thanksgiving. Just like when he left Elon College that very morning. Lenny Stadler never looked back.

If he had, he would have seen a middle-aged guitar

builder, staring at the front door of his music store, tears streaming down his flushed face.

*C*hapter Nine

"And do not be conformed to this world, but be transformed by the renewing of your mind, that you may prove what is that good and acceptable and perfect will of God."

Romans 12:2

*C*ool John Vassilou was driving his seven-year-old Chevy van north on I-95. His destination was Hackettstown, New Jersey. His goal was to hook up two of his best friends in the hopes that a guitarist from industrial New Jersey and a bass player from rural North Carolina could make beautiful music together.

Lenny Stadler, was riding shotgun, keeping an eye out for state troopers, and manning the eight-track. He ejected a *Blood, Sweat and Tears* tape, replacing it with *The Allman Brothers.*

"Listen to these guys, John. They really kick, don't they?"

"Yeah, man," John agreed. "They ain't bad. But you can be better."

"You really think so?" Stadler asked.

"Think so? I know so. We just have to find you the right group of guys to blend with. Don't get me wrong," John continued. "*Blackberry Hill* was a good enough group if all you want to do is hang out around Greensboro, but if we get the right combination, people will be sliding your eight-tracks into their players this time next year."

"Now you're talking," Lenny agreed, draining his bottle of beer, rolling down the van window and tossing it at a passing billboard.

"You missed," John needled him.

"Yeah," Lenny countered. "All this talk of stardom has got me all hepped up. Maybe I need to mellow out a little."

He opened the glove compartment and dug around through the maps and assorted papers until he found a small marijuana cigarette, which he immediately lit. Sweet, pungent smoke filled the vehicle as he took several quick blows and then offered the joint to his friend—and personal roadie.

"I shouldn't smoke pot while I'm driving," he commented, accepting the cigarette and taking a deep toke, nonetheless.

"Why not?" Lenny asked. "Afraid it will cause you to have a wreck?"

"No," John answered, laughing. "It will make me hungry, and if we have to stop and eat we will never get to Hackettstown. We've already stopped about a dozen times today for you to get rid of all that beer you've been drinking."

Lenny ignored this remark and changed tapes again, this time inserting the newest album by an up-and-coming group called *Rare Earth*. "Come on John," he pleaded, "you really think I can make it big?"

"Absolutely!" John insisted. "Wait until you hear old Charlie play that guitar. You two will be sensational together. Then all we'll need is a good drummer and somebody to sing lead and we'll be good to go."

"That's not all we need," Lenny countered. "We need a new sound. We don't want to sound like everybody else. We want to be unique. We want people to turn on the radio, hear our music, and know right away who we are."

John laughed at that last remark. "I think you're getting a little ahead of the game, aren't you. First we have to put together a group and then we have to get on the radio."

"Concerts," Lenny said to him, as if John hadn't even spoken. "I want to do concerts. I'm tired of playing in these clubs and two-bit college dances. People go to those places to drink and talk to their friends and dance. We're just background noise. People go to concerts to listen to the music. That's what I want to do. I want to play concerts. I want to play the big arenas. I want to fill up the *Omni* in Atlanta and the coliseum in Charlotte with people who come just to hear me lay down my complex bass lines."

"You planning on being a solo act?" Lenny's buddy teased him.

"You know what I mean, John. I want it all."

Lenny closed his eyes and let the euphoria of the alcohol and drugs and dreams of stardom encompass his body. Without realizing it he drifted off to sleep. When he opened his eyes he was in the driveway of a modest home, staring into the friendly eyes of a tall lanky person whom John introduced as Charlie.

"Pleased to meet you," Charlie said. "Want to go out back and play some music?"

"That's what we drove 600 miles to do," Lenny responded. "But can I please use the bathroom first?"

Both Charlie and John laughed at the blunt practicality of Lenny's statement. "I guess that might be a good idea," Charlie agreed. "And if I know John," he added, "I bet you guys could use something to munch on, too."

About a half hour later the three music lovers were situated in the makeshift apartment over Charlie's New Jersey garage. Lenny had quickly learned that what John had told him about Charlie was true. He wasn't much of a conversationalist. After the initial introductions he had very little to say. When he plugged in his amp and began to play his guitar, however, Lenny quickly realized that John had been right on the mark about Charlie's talent level, too. In short, the boy could flat play.

Lenny listened at first, and then joined in, as his new acquaintance led him through song after song from the fringes of the Top 40 charts. Lenny realized that Charlie, like Lenny himself, liked music with an edge. Pretty soon the duo was going beyond the bounds of recorded music. They began to ad-lib and create music as they went. They seemed to have a ready-made chemistry, almost as if each had been practicing for this moment for years. Sustained by beer and weed they played far into the night while John sat and listened, glowing with pride at having put these two talents together. At some point they all crashed, and when they awakened, it was the middle of the next day.

"Let's go to the city," John suggested, after the trio had cleaned up, eaten, and gotten used to the idea that they had lived to see another day.

"What city?" Lenny asked.

"What city?," John answered. "New York City! It's just across the river, ain't it?" he asked of their host Charlie, who had lived in New Jersey for some years without finding too many reasons to visit the metropolis that was, indeed, just across the river.

"Yeah," he answered, "it's over there. Just across the George Washington Bridge. But why do you want to go there? It's too big and too crowded. We should just stay here and play music some more. We sounded pretty good last night."

"I've got an idea," Lenny interjected. "Why don't you show us around this town. You can introduce us to your friends. Do you know any good-looking girls you can fix us up with?"

"Not really," Charlie responded to the last inquiry first. "I can't hardly fix myself up."

"Come on," John insisted. "We're going to the city. I don't think Lenny has ever been out of North Carolina and we're going to show him the sights."

"I've been out of North Carolina," Lenny insisted. "I've been to Myrtle Beach lots of times, and I used to go to Nashville with my dad for music conventions.

"Shoot," Lenny continued, "I have too been to New York. My folks took my sister, Judy, and me to see Mickey Mantle and Roger Maris play in Yankee Stadium one time."

"Well, you were a kid then, so we're going back now."

At John's insistence, they all piled into the van. Charlie sat in the front seat to navigate and Lenny took up residence in the back. As they drove among the unfamiliar turf, in awe of the giant skyscrapers surrounding them, they talked about music and creating a new sound and making it big in rock-and-roll.

"I was in a group called *Blackfoot*," Charlie related. "We could gather up those guys and start it back up again. We were pretty good. That's what we need to do."

"What we need to do," interposed John, "is get Medlocke to hook up with us."

"Who is Medlocke?" Lenny questioned from the back seat.

"Can't get him," Charlie insisted. "I talked to him a few weeks ago. He's down in Florida with some group in Jacksonville. He thinks they are going big time."

"Who is Medlocke," Lenny repeated.

Again he was ignored by the duo in the front seat.

"Well, you never know until you ask," John said, then realizing he had no idea where he was driving, asked Charlie for guidance.

"I don't know where we are, man," Charlie told him. "I don't come over here unless someone makes me."

While Lenny sat in the back seat regretting that he was completely sober for his first real New York experience and wondering who in the world Medlocke was, John took turn after turn, trying to navigate the maze that was New

York City traffic.

As Lenny looked out the tinted window of the van, he couldn't help but notice that the towering skyscrapers had given way to smaller and seedier looking buildings and that the makeup of the people on the streets had changed considerably. There were fewer and fewer white faces and business suits. In fact, everywhere he looked he saw black faces. Instead of striding purposefully down the streets, clutching shopping bags and brief cases, more and more of these people were standing idly on street corners. Many stared openly at the beat-up blue van with North Carolina plates.

"Oh no!" John moaned as he saw flashing blue lights in his rear view mirror. "Cops!"

"Is everybody clean?" Charlie asked, patting down his own pockets to make sure he wasn't carrying any forgotten contraband.

"Yeah, man. We're clean," Lenny assured him. "John said we smoked our last two joints just before we got to your place last night. I wish those cops would say something to me. I'll invite them to search this whole van. Ain't no law against having empty beer cans in the floor is there?"

"Let me do the talking," John warned his friend nervously, as he rolled down his window for the approaching officer.

"Yes sir," he said to the policeman as he leaned into the driver's side window and peered inside the van, looking disdainfully at its cluttered contents and long-haired occupants.

"Do you boys know where you are?" the officer asked.

"We're in New York, aren't we?" John answered, desperately hoping he didn't sound like a complete smart aleck.

"You're in Harlem," the cop said. "And you have no business being here at all. You are the wrong color and you are in the wrong place and this is the wrong time."

"Yes sir," John responded. "I was just saying the same thing to my friends. In fact, we are looking for Hackettstown, and if you could just direct us out of here, that's where we'll go."

"I'm from Hackettstown," Charlie interjected, trying to be of help.

"You boys been drinking?" the officer asked, looking suspiciously at the empty Budweiser cans strewn throughout the van's interior.

"No sir," John assured him. "All those are left over from yesterday."

"You don't have any drugs in this vehicle do you?" the policeman asked.

Lenny, for some inexplicable reason, decided this would be a good time for him to break his silence. "We don't have any drugs, officer. You can search us if you don't believe me. Just search the whole van if you want to. We don't have any drugs. No sir. None at all."

John turned and gave Lenny a look that said, "Shut your stupid mouth! " He said nothing. The look said it all.

The cop stood at the window for a long time, trying

to decide whether or not he should take the long- haired young loudmouth in the back seat up on his offer. Finally, he decided against it. Instead he gave them a long lecture on using common sense while driving in New York City— along with directions out of Harlem and back to the New Jersey side of the river.

Once they were safely on the west side of the Hudson River, John reached under his seat and pulled out a plastic bag containing about two pounds of Colombian Gold. "Next time, Lenny, when I say let me do the talking, you'd better let me do the talking."

Charlie, who hadn't said a word since their close en-counter with the NYPD started laughing uncontrollably.

Lenny, who was angry at his roadie for lying to him in the first place, but too embarrassed by his own stupidity to say so, decided to change the subject.

"Now where in Florida do we have to go to get this guy Medlocke?" he asked.

"Jacksonville," Charlie responded.

"Y'all sure he's worth the trip?" Lenny asked.

"You bet!" John replied. "When we get to Florida, you'll find out."

Chapter Ten

"But those who desire to be rich fall into temptation and a snare, and into many foolish and harmful lusts which drown men in destruction and perdition."

I Timothy 6:9

"*L*eonard Skinner?" Lenny Stadler asked incredulously, as he tossed a wop-sided baseball at a dirty and ragged stuffed cat—missing his target, for the umpteenth straight time. He and John and Charlie had finally caught up with Medlocke, after a journey of 1000 miles, two flat tires, a busted water pump, and another brush with the law in Macon, Georgia, which resulted in a speeding ticket but, thankfully, no search of the car and, therefore, no additional charges. He was on the boardwalk, in Jacksonville Beach, Florida, rehearsing for a weekend engagement with the local group that, in Medlocke's mind, was just about to be discovered by a national talent scout.

"Not 'Leonard Skinner,'" Medlocke replied, throwing a baseball himself and knocking his third straight cat right off the shelf. "*Lynard Skynard*. L-Y-N-Y-R-D--S-K-Y-N-Y-R-D," he spelled out the unusual name.

"You have a guy in your group named Lynyrd Skynyrd?" Stadler asked, throwing his last ball and, naturally, missing the entire target.

"He's not in our group," Medlocke explained. "He's a high school gym teacher, and a real mean one, too. And his name is not Lynyrd Skynyrd, it's Leonard Skinner. We changed the spelling around so he couldn't sue us."

"Why in the world did you name your group after a

high school coach?" Lenny felt compelled to ask.

"Because he hates long hair and hard rock," Medlocke replied, indicating to the game operator behind the counter that the giant purple panda on the top shelf would be adequate reward for his pitching skill. "He's always getting on everybody about their hair and spending too much time on music and not enough time hitting the books. We decided to name our band after him just to try and tick him off."

"Let's take a walk on the beach," Lenny suggested.

"Here, baby," Medlocke said, handing the giant purple panda to the first cute blonde they passed.

She and her friend, a stunning redhead, giggled as they looked back over their shoulders at the two jean clad guys, who each had hair longer than the girls themselves. "Do you think they just flew in from Haight Asbury?" the blonde asked her friend.

"Either that or they don't realize that they are about six months late for Halloween," she replied.

"Or six months early," the blonde quipped. The girls laughed at their own cleverness and continued strolling in the opposite direction as Stadler and Medlocke made their way down to the sand.

The waves of the gray Atlantic crashed against the shore, spraying the faces of the two musicians as they walked and talked. Lenny Stadler had taken an instant liking to his counterpart as soon as they stood in the doorway of the deserted boardwalk nightclub where *Lynyrd Skynyrd* was practicing. He knew instinctively that Medlocke's style would complement him and Charlie. Stadler was convinced that Medlocke would add one more piece to the puzzle he and John Vee began putting together when they left Reidsville and he was determined that he would convince him to abandon his high school friends and throw in with his group.

The two walked in silence for a while. Finally, Lenny spoke. "Look, man," he intoned. "I don't think you understand what we are talking about here. We're not going to be a high school garage band, playing the college circuit. We're going to make the big time. We're going to show the rest of this country how the Southern boys play rock-and-roll music. We're going to make records and play the big concert halls. If you'll sign on with Charlie and me, there's no telling where we might end up. No telling!"

Medlocke was more than a little offended at the insinuation he needed Stadler to make the big time, and said so. "Listen here," he said indignantly. "I'm already in a good band. You heard us play back there. We're good. Why should I ditch my friends and join up with somebody I don't even know?"

"Because you know Charlie," Lenny countered, "and John. John knows music. He told you the same thing I did. And you heard how good Charlie and I were while your boys were taking a break back there. You were dying to grab your guitar and jam with us. The three of us were made for one another. All we need is a drummer. We'll find one somewhere—a good one--and then head back north. After we've practiced a few months and put together some of our own stuff, we'll be own our way."

"Back north?" Medlocke replied. "You can forget that. I ain't going back to New Jersey with you or anybody else. I like it down South, where it's nice and warm and the girls are nice and sweet."

"Not north to New Jersey," Lenny said. "We'll make our headquarters in North Carolina. We can stay in Reidsville. My old man has a house we can use and he owns a music store. He can help us with equipment and stuff, and we'll be halfway between the Northeast and Florida. We can pick up gigs all along the Atlantic coast."

Medlocke was wavering, Lenny could tell. He decided to press his advantage. "Look, Medlocke. You're playing in a band with the same guys you played with at the high school sock hops. You're named for a high school gym teacher for goodness sake. Those guys aren't going anywhere. A weekend gig in Dothan, Alabama will be the highlight of their career. You can have more than that."

The two walked slowly up the beach in silence, each lost in his own thoughts. It was Medlocke who broke the silence. "I know one," he said.

"One what?" Lenny asked.

"A drummer. I know a drummer. A good one. His name is Jackson. I think we can find him in Atlanta. Atlanta is on the way to North Carolina, isn't it?" he asked, a slight smile playing at the corners of his mouth.

"Then you're in?" Lenny asked excitedly. "You're really in?"

"Yeah," Medlocke answered. "I think I'm in. But there's just one thing."

"What's that, man?" Lenny asked.

"Girls. I require lots and lots of female companionship. The prettiest girls in the world are right here in Jacksonville. They are toned and tanned and hot to trot. And they like me. You can take me away from Lynyrd Skynyrd, but if you take me away from all these long tanned legs, there'd better be lots more to take their place."

"Not a problem," Lenny assured him. "Let's go find John and tell him to put some gas in that old van of his. We got to go to Atlanta and find this drummer."

Chapter Eleven

"Come, let us build ourselves a city, and a tower, whose top is in the heavens; let us make a name for ourselves."

Genesis 11:4

"*M*an, what a cool place!" Cool John Vee was catching his first glimpse of Underground Atlanta, which in 1972 was the most happening place in the whole Southeast. He, Lenny, Charlie, and Medlocke, were strolling the crowded sidewalks beneath the South's unofficial capital city, sticking their heads inside the dozens of nightclubs and eateries and staring appreciatively at the hundreds of good-looking girls who were walking around the giant complex. Some were with dates but most were with groups of other girls, all looking for a good time in Hotlanta.

The foursome stepped inside a place called *Ruby Red's Warehouse*, where a blind albino was playing the keys off a white grand piano. After listening to two or three songs they wandered out the door and across the street to a nightclub that was overflowing with college-aged kids, all holding plastic cups of beer. The banner above the door challenged the patrons to "Drink or Drown" every Thursday night, and advertised draft beer for a quarter a cup.

"Y'all want a carton of milk?" asked a sweet young thing with an exaggerated Southern accent, standing just inside the door.

"Why in the world would we want milk when beer is a quarter a glass?" asked Medlocke, who always welcomed the opportunity to talk with sweet young things.

"Why, to coat your stomach, of course, so you can drink more."

"Yeah, Medlocke," chimed in John. "Don't you know anything?"

"We won't be staying long enough to need any milk," Lenny offered. "We'll just have one beer and be on our way. We're looking for a buddy of ours—a guy named Jackson. He's supposed to be playing the drums at a place called *Mother Fletcher's*. You know where it is?"

The waitress seemed disappointed that the boys wouldn't be staying longer, but brought them their beers and gave them directions to their destination.

"Pay the lady, Charlie," Stadler said as he, John, and Medlocke grabbed the cups of beer off the waitress's tray and hurried out the door, leaving the one member of the group who hadn't said a word to pay for the brews. He did so good naturedly, placing two one dollar bills on the girl's tray and telling her to keep the change.

Back outside he caught up with his friends who had stopped to watch an organ grinder and his monkey, who was working the crowd by walking up to each person and tipping his little red hat, in hopes of getting a quarter for his troubles.

"That monkey's better paid than we are," Medlocke joked.

"Yeah," Lenny allowed, "but not for long. Let's go find your buddy and see if he can play the drums."

"He can play," Medlocke assured him.

A few minutes later the group found themselves inside yet another nightclub that was bursting at the seams with people in their early twenties. They were able to push past the three-deep crowd at the bar and seat themselves at a tiny round table in the back corner of the room. The room was dark and full of smoke, which didn't bother any of the four, who were all right at home in such an atmosphere.

On stage the house band was playing a song by a British band that none of the boys were familiar with. It had a decent beat, but wasn't particularly appealing to them.

"That's him," Medlocke said, indicating the group's drummer who looked a bit bored as he went through the motions of keeping time with the music. "You can't tell what he can do as long as they are playing that garbage," Medlocke added, reading Stadler's mind. "Just keep listening. He'll show you something in a minute."

Lenny did just that. He listened to the group, that was average at best, and studied the drummer. It was obvious that he knew what he was doing by the effortless way he handled his set of instruments, but in no way indicated that he was worthy of the praise Medlocke had heaped upon him on the long drive up from Jacksonville. In addition to studying the drummer, Jackson, Lenny couldn't help but pay attention to the group's bass player, whom Lenny decided right away couldn't carry his guitar strap.

"There ain't much to this bunch," Lenny offered during a break between songs. In fact, he was about to risk offending the newest recruit to his own musical group by suggesting they stop in some of Underground's other night spots and see if they could recruit a more inspiring drummer.

Before he could do that, however, the house band's lead singer announced into the microphone, "Now, ladies and gentleman, we're going to do a little number to showcase our drummer, who is not a regular member of our group, but is sitting in with us tonight."

Without another word the group went right into the 1968 classic, *Wipeout*, which was, of course, a drummer's dream. Lenny was mesmerized. When the spotlight fell on Medlocke's friend, Jackson, he became a different person. He came alive and he turned his drum-set into a living, breathing creature. His hands were everywhere at once. Sweat was pouring profusely from every pore of his body as the band completely energized by the drummer's performance, played the song over and over and over.

The audience began standing and cheering and flicking their cigarette lighters and holding their flames high in the air. Lenny and John and Charlie were screaming and stomping and whistling along with the rest of the crowd. When the number finally ended, Lenny felt as spent as Jackson, who was breathing hard and nodding to the audience in appreciation for their response.

Medlocke smiled smugly at Lenny and asked over the roar of the crowd, "Well, what do you think?"

"The best I ever heard," Lenny responded honestly.

"That guy is the best I ever heard. You think we can get him?"

"Get him?" Medlocke repeated. "He filled in here tonight for about twelve dollars, and I bet that's the most money he's made in a week. All we have to do is ask."

Two hours later, John, Lenny, Medlocke, Charlie, and their nameless group's newest member, Jackson Spires, were sitting around a table at *The Nitery,* the hot Peachtree Street nightclub that was the home of Morgana, Atlanta's most well known entertainer, who had become famous by running onto baseball fields across the Major Leagues and planting kisses on the cheeks of unsuspecting superstars.

"Okay, gang. We gotta have a name," Lenny Stadler was saying to the group, who were so excited about their new endeavor that they were hardly paying any attention at all to the young waitress that was trying desperately to attract their attention--and their tips.

"I always liked *Blackfoot*," Charlie suggested. "Don't see anything wrong with resurrecting *Blackfoot*."

"*Blackfoot* suits me," Medlocke agreed.

"Me, too," Jackson chimed in.

"Wait a minute, now," Lenny said. "This isn't going to be your same old *Blackfoot*, Charlie, because I'm in it now. We're going to be a whole new group with a whole new sound. We can still play that British hard rock, but we're going to play it with a definite Southern accent. We've all got to understand that."

Charlie just smiled at Lenny. So did John and Jackson. Only Medlocke spoke, but he was smiling, too. "Okay, Stadler. We're going to be different and we're going to be better, and we're going to rock the music world. But unless you can offer up the name of your high school gym teacher or somebody better, I think we're going to do it as *Blackfoot.*"

"I'll drink to that," Stadler said, hoisting his drink. The other four at the table clinked their glasses against his and *Blackfoot* was born.

And they drained their glasses and left, without ever seeing Morgana.

Chapter Twelve

*"Do not love the world or the things in the world . . . for all
that is in the world--the lust of the flesh, the lust of the eyes,
and the pride of life--is not of the Father but is of the world.
And the world is passing away, and the lust of it; but he who
does the will of God abides forever."*

I John 2:15-17

*7*he next few months were like a dream come true for Lenny Stadler. He and the other members of *Blackfoot* threw themselves into their music with more enthusiasm— and more effort—than they had devoted to any previous endeavor. Twelve hour rehearsals were the norm and from the very beginning the distinct blend of styles, talents, and personalities began to produce a unique sound. A new style of music was beginning to take hold in America—a blend of blues and British rock which would come to be known as "Southern Rock," and the *Blackfoot* boys were determined to establish themselves on the leading edge of the waves that would engulf the nation during the early 1970s.

Leonard Stadler grudgingly began to forgive his son for dropping out of school and starting a band. He still didn't approve of his son's appearance, but spent less time criticizing him for it once he saw how serious Lenny and his new-found friends were about their music. He was, in fact, an invaluable supporter of the group, providing them with living quarters and practice space, and even discounted equipment that they never could have afforded otherwise.

Dorothy Stadler wasn't happy that her son was not in school, but she was very happy that he was at home and not constantly wandering around the country full time. She was able to ignore his increasingly deviant behavior and, in fact, convinced herself that he was the same old Lenny, just in different packaging. She actually enjoyed being around his friends who looked really rough but were always very polite, especially when she invited them over for a home cooked meal, which she tried to do at least once a week.

Johnny Bullock was a different story altogether. No matter how nearby Lenny and his friends were or how hard they worked or how polite they were, he was convinced that his grandson was a lost soul who had abandoned his Christian upbringing. Even worse, Johnny was convinced that Lenny had abandoned God and that if he had ever had a personal relationship with Jesus Christ, he had long since abandoned that, too—in favor of the harlot, rock-and-roll music, and all its trappings.

While Lenny's father was encouraged by the industry his son was exhibiting and his mother was trying to pretend everything was the same as it had always been, his grandfather was determined to do everything in his power, whatever that might be, to bring his grandson back to the throne of grace. He began praying before sunrise, most mornings as early as 4 a.m., that Lenny would have his eyes opened and see the light of the Risen Lord. The last words he uttered before going to sleep each night were pleas that the way of the cross would lead Lenny back home.

His grandfather was determined not to rely on intercessory prayer to touch Lenny's heart. Every time he saw Lenny he told him that he was praying for him and urged him to give his life to God before it was too late. Lenny, of course, didn't want to hear it, so he didn't. He avoided his grandfather like the plague. He refused to go to his house for any reason, and if his grandfather showed up at the music store or at home while Lenny was there, he left. He didn't allow himself to care if he was hurting someone who loved him so much. In the back of his mind Lenny knew that accepting Jesus Christ would mean that he could no longer enjoy the drugs, alcohol, and sex that were becoming more and more readily available to him with every venue *Blackfoot* played.

And *Blackfoot* did play. They found a booking agent that kept them busy throughout the Carolinas every Friday and Saturday night, and often during the week. They weren't high paying jobs, but they all paid in cash and they gave the band an opportunity to refine their music and try out new original songs. There were lots of fringe benefits, too.

The crowds, for instance. Everywhere they went, the crowds really loved *Blackfoot's* music. With their long hair and rough look, *Blackfoot* was a part of the counter-culture their audiences wished they could join. Lenny and the others thrived on the cheers and adulation being heaped upon them by the appreciative crowds.

The hard rock music just seemed to feel better to some of the band members if they were high when they played it. Marijuana was readily available and Lenny forgot what it was like to go onstage without a buzz. After every concert there were girls who were so taken with the long-haired musicians that they were willing to offer just about anything to spend time with them, and the musicians were always more than happy to indulge themselves. Stronger drugs were available, too, and Lenny was willing to experiment with whatever someone promised would make him feel good.

Without even realizing it, he had entered a downward spiral. He was becoming a part of a cycle that would plague so many performers of his day. He would drink in the afternoons and then smoke dope to mellow out; take pills to pep him up and pills to bring him down; and he'd take anything else that was offered to him, especially if it was offered by a beautiful young girl who insisted that her drug of choice would enhance the intimacy she was about to provide.

In short, he was quickly becoming the lost soul that only his grandfather recognized he was becoming. He didn't even recognize it himself. He just knew that he was playing music and experiencing a wider variety of pleasures of the flesh than he ever knew existed. The only thing he needed to make his life whole, in his mind, was for his band to hit it big, and he was convinced that that day couldn't be far away.

On an otherwise normal Thursday afternoon, Lenny got a phone call from *Blackfoot's* booking agency indicating that the group's big break was closer than even he might have anticipated.

It was shortly after lunchtime—or at least what would

be lunchtime for ordinary people—which would make it right after breakfast for Lenny and his friends. They were practicing in back of Leonard Stadler's music store—in between sessions of griping about having the weekend free.

"It doesn't make sense, man," Jackson Spires was saying to the band as a whole and no one in particular. "Money is money and we should have taken that high school gig."

"Nah, man," Lenny rebutted. "We agreed that we were going to lay off those kinds of gigs. Our time would be better spent staying right here and working on our new songs than driving halfway to Kalamazoo to play for a bunch of teeny boppers."

"Yeah," Medlocke added. "Besides, we're just inviting trouble playing at those high school dances. We can't really be ourselves. Know what I mean?"

Inspired by this remark, Charlie spoke up. "Yeah, Medlocke, we know exactly what you mean. Those girls could cause real trouble."

Everyone in the group laughed at Charlie's remark.

"Let's play that last song one more time," Lenny suggested. "I want to try a new bass line I've been working on."

Before they could resume practice, however, John rushed through the door. His flushed face and rapid breathing indicated that he was even more excited than usual.

"You boys want to take a trip to Asheville tomorrow night?" he asked.

"Asheville?" the band members all asked at once.

"What's in Asheville?" Medlocke added.

"Only a chance to open for *The Edgar Winter Group* and *Black Oak Arkansas*," John responded smugly.

Everyone in the room started speaking at once as John was bombarded with questions.

"Edgar Winter?"

"Are you for real John? You'd better not be putting us on!"

"Why would they call us the day before a gig?"

"How much will we get paid?"

And again, "Edgar Winter? Are you for real John."

"Hold it! Hold it!" John pleaded, holding both arms in front of his face, as if warding off blows. "One question at a time. Here's the deal.

"Edgar Winter is playing in the Asheville Civic Auditorium tomorrow night. His warmup band canceled at the last minute. Somebody got busted and the group's equipment got impounded, or something. We are the closest band to Asheville that plays music compatible to Winter's, so our agent called us. And it pays 200 bucks and all the pills and smoke you want. You're on your own for finding chicks," he added, smiling facetiously in Charlie's direction.

John waited a while to let the news sink in before asking, "What do you say, guys? Are we in or out?"

"Are you crazy?" Lenny asked. "We're in man! You know we're in! Call that guy back and tell him that *Blackfoot* is on the way!"

They were, too. In more ways than one.

Chapter Thirteen

"Do you not know that friendship with the world is enmity with God? Whoever therefore wants to be a friend of the world makes himself an enemy of God."

James 4:4

*L*enny Stadler's hands were sweating, his mouth was dry, and his palms were sweating. Thirty-six hours earlier he had been practicing with his buddies in the back of his father's music store, and now he was on stage in a giant coliseum. There were thousands of people out there who had come to hear Edgar Winter. Edgar Winter was known all across the nation. He had made it. He filled the big arenas and recorded songs that were played on the radio everywhere. And all those people who dug Edgar Winter were about to hear an hour's worth of *Blackfoot* before they got to hear the band they came to hear. And Lenny was scared to death they wouldn't like what they heard.

Oddly enough, as he waited for his band to be introduced and the curtain to go up, he thought of something his grandfather used to say. "Be careful what you wish for, son. You just might get it."

Lenny couldn't help but laugh. "Well," he thought to himself, "This is definitely what I wished for—for a long time. I just hope we can make the most of it."

He looked around the stage at his group's equipment that was interspersed on the stage among the more elaborate setup of the main attraction. He asked his roadie, John, if everything was working. He knew before asking that it was. John was becoming much more than a roadie; he was almost like the group's manager and he knew the sound of good music. John wanted this night to be a success as much as any of the musicians.

"Finest kind," he responded.

Lenny had smoked a joint ten minutes earlier, in an attempt to calm his nerves. He found himself wanting another, but was afraid of becoming too mellow. Besides, it was almost showtime and he couldn't be seen toking on a joint while he played. "Or can I?" he allowed himself to think.

"Hey, Stadler," Medlocke called out across the stage. "You think there will be any good-looking chicks out there tonight?"

Lenny laughed. "Well, it won't be like the boardwalk in Jacksonville," he responded, "but Carolina girls are pretty hot."

"You guys better just worry about sounding good," Charlie suggested. "This will be the most people any of us have ever played in front of. We'd better not screw it up."

Jackson Spires just grinned and gave his cymbal a spirited lick with a drumstick.

Just then the show's producer appeared, as from nowhere. "It's showtime, fellas," he shouted to the nervous group.

As if on cue, the house lights dimmed and the crowd cheered, and then quieted themselves as the voice of the public address announcer came over the giant overhead speakers. "Coming to you from Reidsville, North Carolina," the deep melodious voice boomed, "we've got *Blackfoot!*"

Lenny thought it was the coolest thing he had ever heard as the announcer's final syllable reverberated through the big hall, as the curtain was drawn and blindingly bright lights illuminated the guys on stage.

"Hit it!" Medlocke called out, and the band immediately went into their first number. Lenny was in a trance for the next fifty minutes. He actually felt like he was having an out-of-body experience. He could tell from the very first note that the band was clicking like they had never clicked before, and they were giving the crowd exactly what they came to hear—hard Southern rock, but hard Southern rock like they had never heard before.

All four musicians completely abandoned themselves, becoming totally emersed in the beat of the music--their music—the music they had been working on together for months, and for years as individuals, to create. They were on, and they knew it. The crowd absolutely loved them, and they knew that, too. They forgot about where they were and who was watching them perform and which big name star was waiting in the wings to put on the "real show." They just played their music.

Lenny was alive on the bass, his fingers manipulating the four strings as if they were a part of him. Charlie and Medlocke were making their guitars talk and Medlocke was as one with the audience as he made verbal love to the microphone in front of him. Jackson Spires played the drums as only Jackson Spires could play the drums. Lenny allowed himself to look around the stage and was surprised to see the passion on the faces of his friends. Only when he realized that the rest of the band was drenched in sweat did he notice that his shirt was also wringing wet and sticking to his body. Perspiration poured from his long hair and dripped off his mustache. He didn't care. He had found nirvana, and for *Blackfoot*, their moment had arrived.

And then the producer shouted, "That's it, guys! Last number!"

It seemed to Lenny that they had just gotten started, but they went immediately into the song they had saved for last and gave it everything they had. When they had finished, the entire coliseum crowd was screaming, clapping their hands, stomping their feet, and swaying with the music. The spotlights went down just before the curtain closed and Lenny could see hundreds of cigarette lighters flickering in the audience, held high in tribute to the music they had just made.

"Great job, guys!" the anonymous producer shouted as soon as the curtain was pulled tight. "Now hurry up and get your stuff moved. Edgar goes on in 15 minutes."

Lenny and the other members of *Blackfoot* could still hear the crowd screaming and shouting in unison, "*Blackfoot! Blackfoot! Blackfoot!*"

"Let them play another song," a voice said from the back of the stage. The producer turned to protest and realized that Edgar Winter, himself, had made the suggestion.

"You guys got another song?" he asked furtively?

"Heck yeah!" Medlocke interjected. "We've got all the songs you want."

"Encore!" the producer shouted and once again the curtains were opened to the glare of the lights and the cheering crowd.

Lenny was completely drained when the band finished the extra number, but not too exhausted to respond when Edgar Winter came up to him and shook his hand. He also handed him a card from a local hotel with a room number scribbled across it.

"Come to my suite after the show," he said. "We're having a little party."

"Sure," Lenny replied, trying to sound cool about the whole thing, as if he and his friends partied with national recording celebrities every night. "I think we can make it." Then, afraid that he'd sounded unappreciative, amended his response by adding. "Yeah. We'll be there. Thanks, man."

As the members of *Blackfoot* scurried around getting their amps and instruments off the stage, a guy in a white shirt and necktie approached Lenny. "Can you guys open for Edgar down in Charlotte tomorrow night?"

"Are you serious, man?" Lenny asked him.

"Sure," he replied. "You guys were great. You rocked the house. The crowd loved you."

"We're right there," Lenny answered, and then added, "We still get 200 bucks?"

"Yeah," Mr. Whiteshirt answered. "You'll still get 200

bucks."

The members of *Blackfoot* were still riding a natural high as they made their way to the penthouse suite of the luxurious Asheville hotel. As they got off the elevator, which had stopped at the top floor, a middle-aged man in a red uniform looked disdainfully at their long hair and sloppy jeans. "Are you guests here?" he asked haughtily.

"Yeah," Lenny replied. "We're guests of Edgar Winter." He fished the card he had been given out of his pocket and handed it to the disgruntled floor man.

"End of the hall," he said resignedly. "Double doors on the right."

The boys couldn't believe their eyes when they walked into the large suite of rooms. The air was thick with incense and blacklights had been placed in each receptacle, giving an eerie glow to the entire room. Rock music emitted from an invisible source and the room was packed with long-haired entertainers, roadies, groupies, and hangers-on. Two-thirds of the people in the room were girls. Most had long, straight hair and short, short skirts. All had that glazed and dazed look that indicated they were strung out.

A beautiful brunette immediately approached Lenny, grabbing his arm. "I know you," she said to him, "but you don't know me."

"You do?" he said, trying to figure out who she was and why she knew him.

"Yes I do," she said. "You're that guy that plays the

bass so good for *Blackfoot*. I watched you all night."

Now having pretty girls be impressed by his playing ability was nothing new to Lenny. There were easy marks at every venue. But he had never run into one as forward as this lovely lady whose name he didn't even know.

"Come on back here," she cooed in his ear, pulling him through the crowded living room.

"Where are you taking me?" Lenny asked.

"To the buffet," she replied.

The brunette led Lenny into the kitchen. The double sink was full of ice and beer. Two large coolers, also full of beer, were on the floor. The counter beside the sink held bottles of every type of whiskey Lenny had ever heard of and several that he hadn't. And on the table in the middle of the room were plastic trays filled with marijuana cigarette and pills of every color and description.

"What's your pleasure?" Lenny's self-appointed hostess asked him.

He just stared at the smorgasbord of illegal drugs, not even knowing what most of the pills were.

His companion mistook his hesitation and quickly said, "I didn't know what kind of mood you'd be in after such a hot show. I thought you were probably all keyed up and would need to wind down a little. If you want some cocaine or LSD, we won't have to go far."

"No," Lenny responded. "This is fine. In fact," he added, "Why don't you surprise me. I'll just have what you're having."

The brunette picked up two "yellow jackets" from the plastic tray and filled two Dixie cups with Wild Turkey whiskey. She popped one of the pills into her mouth and the other into Lenny's. "Cheers," she said, handing him one of the cups of amber colored liquor. They clicked the cups together and immediately downed the contents in one gulp.

"They say you shouldn't take these things together," the girl confided, "but I do it all the time and it's never hurt me. And it makes you feel so good," she added.

When Lenny awoke the next day he didn't remember exactly where he was or how he got there. He opened his eyes slightly, adjusting to his surroundings slowly. Then he remembered bits and pieces of the night before—the party, the concert, the excitement of being on stage in a big arena. And then he remembered that he and the band were driving that afternoon from Asheville to Charlotte to do it all again.

"I wonder what her name was?" he asked himself with a chuckle as he thought about his new acquaintance from the night before. "And I wonder if she'll be in Charlotte tonight?"

At just about the time Lenny was getting out of bed, his grandfather , a hundred miles and light years away, was bowing his head to give thanks for his daily bread. After blessing his food and asking forgiveness for his sins he added, "and please, God, touch Lenny's heart. I know he's in a bad way right now and I know he's struggling. I know how much he needs you, Lord, and I beg you to just touch his heart."

Johnny Bullock had no way of knowing it, but things would get a lot worse before they got better.

Chapter Fourteen

*"For what profit is it to a man if he gains the whole world,
and loses his own soul?"*

Matthew 16:26

*L*ife became a whirlwind for Lenny Stadler and the other members of *Blackfoot* after their smashing debut with *The Edgar Winter Group* and *Black Oak Arkansas.* They were good. They knew they were good, and had known it all along. They were all accomplished musicians and their talent blended perfectly. Each member had been preparing himself for a long time, and when their music meshed, it was magical.

They became a regular opening act for Edgar Winter and actually began to develop a fan base of their own— complete with groupies who would follow them from town to town and gig to gig—always ready to offer drugs and whiskey and anything else the band members might need.

Promoters began to pair *Blackfoot* with other up-and-coming Southern rock groups. They played with *The Allman Brothers Band* and *The Marshall Tucker Band.* Medlocke even got to hook up with his old Jacksonville pals when *Blackfoot* played several gigs with *Lynyrd Skynyrd.* In fact, *Blackfoot* was becoming so popular that it was sometimes hard to tell which band was the warmup act and which was the main attraction.

Lenny became totally engrossed in the hard rock culture. He grew his hair even longer and tried to look as shockingly unkempt as possible every time he took to the stage. He and the band traveled from city to city, playing all along the Eastern seaboard. As their gigs got bigger, so did the pay checks. They graduated from an old run-down van pulling a U-Haul trailer to two new vans and a separate truck for their equipment.

As the band grew more successful, so did the size and intensity of the after-concert parties. Lenny found himself slipping into a dangerous and potentially deadly pattern of using drugs to get high for a performance and drugs to come back down afterward. Then, when he'd meet girls that he wanted to impress—and there were always girls he wanted to impress—he would take more drugs to pick him up and to bring him down or whatever was needed to match their mood.

Gradually, his focus seemed to shift. It wasn't just about making music anymore. It was about instant gratification and pleasure at any price. It should have been the happiest time of Lenny's life because he was actually in the process of living his life's dream. He was on the road with a rock-and-roll band and on the very verge of making the big time. In reality, his life was inexplicably becoming more and more empty and meaningless.

The music, the crowds, the drugs, the girls—none of these things were bringing him the fulfillment he expected. Nonetheless, he fell deeper and deeper into the counterculture of the rock world, convinced that happiness and contentment was as close as the next gig or the next party or the next conquest.

During this time, Lenny met Susan, who was a pure vision. No other word could describe her beauty. She was medium height and slender with big brown eyes, long dark hair, a beautiful smile, and flawless olive toned skin. Lenny met her when the band performed at the University of North Carolina in Greensboro, where she was a student.

The daughter of a Baptist minister, when Susan found herself at college and on her own, she, like so many preacher's kids, decided to take a walk on the wild side of life. Having a long-haired, bass-guitar-playing boyfriend would be the last thing her father would want, so, naturally, it was just what Susan determined to have. Although Susan's company didn't bring peace and contentment to Lenny's life, she made the search a lot more pleasurable.

On a typical early afternoon after a typical night before, John burst into Lenny's hotel room to find him curled up in the bed, buried under a pile of covers.

"Come on, Lenny. Drag your sorry self out of bed. We have to get to the stadium and set up. *Skynyrd* wants to do a sound check at 6:30 and we go on at 7:30, so we have to have our stuff set up and be out of their way by 6:15."

Lenny felt like he had been ridden hard and put away wet. Every fiber of his being hurt, including his hair. "Why does *Skynyrd* get to dictate what time we have our stuff set up?" Lenny asked irritably.

"You know good and well why," John answered. "Because they are the headline act, but don't mention that around Medlocke. He's already ticked because they are on the fast track. They've got a recording contract now and Medlocke said they were working on some song about Alabama that will put them over the top."

"Alabama?" Lenny asked, still hiding under the covers from the bright glare of daylight. "Those guys are all from Jacksonville. Why would they write a song about Alabama?"

"I don't know," John responded. "What difference does it make? All I know is you have to get up and get going."

"Where is Susan?" Lenny asked, suddenly remembering that he had been with his girlfriend at a party the night before. For the life of him, he couldn't remember where they had gone or what they had done after the party.

"She caught a ride back to Greensboro with some friends. Said she had to go to class this morning."

Lenny laughed at that remark. "Well she's a better man than I am if she can party with me all night and still go to school the next day."

Now it was John's turn to laugh. "Nothing about her resembles any man I've ever seen."

"You got that right, brother," Lenny agreed.

She and Lenny were a natural fit and each pushed the other to greater heights—or depths—when it came to partying. There was no drug she wouldn't try and no sensation she didn't want to experience. And Lenny was right there with her, eager to match her step for step.

"Is she driving back down to hear us tonight?" Lenny asked John.

"Negative, man," John answered. "She said her parents were having some sort of anniversary thing this weekend and she had to be there, so she's going home to play 'Little Miss Respectable' tonight."

"Then what are we doing?" Lenny asked, finally swinging his legs over the side of his bed and attempting to stand.

"Don't worry, man. We'll find something to do."

Lenny asked his friend to go out and pick up some food while he showered and got ready to head to the concert venue to set up their equipment. After making Lenny promise three times that he wouldn't climb back in the bed and crash again, John agreed.

Lenny turned the water on full force and adjusted the temperature until the spray was as hot as he could stand it before climbing over the edge of the tub and stepping under the steamy hot water. It felt good on his back and neck and he stood for a long time, just letting the water soak his body and waist-length hair.

As he stood there, under the revitalizing water, he began to think about the night's impending concert. At first he imagined himself on stage, his fingers rapidly moving across the four strings of his bass guitar as the bright house lights shone in his face. Then he began to listen, in his mind, for the noise from the crowd as they stamped and whistled and cheered after every number. He took a deep breath as the hot water continued to pour over his back as he felt the rush that accompanied every such moment.

Then Lenny's mind raced ahead and began thinking about what the evening would bring once the concert was over and the crowd was gone. He was a little bummed out that Susan would not be with him because she was exquisitely beautiful and he loved her company. But there would be plenty of fun to be had, with or without Susan. There was always fun to be had.

And then, for some inexplicable reason, the visions in his mind's eye began to change. Instead of Susan and large concert halls and cheering crowds, Lenny began to see images of his home and family—his mother's face, his father standing behind the counter at his music store in Reidsville, his grandmother and grandfather, eyes closed and heads bowed, saying a prayer over their evening meal.

Lenny's mood changed immediately, the happy glow of his afternoon reverie replaced by an empty feeling in the pit of his stomach. He angrily turned off the pulsating water. As he climbed out of the tub he grabbed a cheap towel and began drying himself off. He was amazed to realize that tears were streaming down his already wet cheeks.

Chapter Fifteen

"For Satan himself transforms himself into an angel of light."

II Corinthians 11:14

7he night started out like most nights. The band was "on" and the crowd was loud and appreciative, calling them back onstage for an encore performance. Backstage, after *Blackfoot* had finished, Medlocke, Charlie, and Jackson Spires indicated that they were going to hang around and listen to the up-and-coming group, *Chicago*, play. Out of the corner of his eye, Lenny caught John making a slicing motion across his throat. Lenny understood immediately that he and John would not be hanging around and told the other band members that he would catch up with them later, back at the hotel.

Lenny followed John out the back door of the concert hall. Waiting for them in the parking lot were two gorgeous girls. Both were very tall and very thin with long straight hair. Both girls were wearing flowing, ankle-length dresses of a dark gauze-type material. One was platinum blonde and had the palest skin Lenny had ever seen. It was almost transparent, and her ice blue eyes gave her a very exotic and unusual appearance. The other girl had a dark complexion. Her hair was jet black and her eyes were dark brown.

"They sure don't like *Chicago*," John said to Lenny, by way of explanation. "They want to take us home."

John and the blonde slid into the front seat of John's van and Lenny climbed into the backseat with the dark-haired girl. As soon as they were underway, she dug around in her purse and produced a joint which she lit and handed to Lenny. He took a deep drag, holding his breath and allowing the sweet, acrid smoke to permeate his body before leaning forward and handing it to John's newfound friend in the front seat. After a very short ride, they found themselves at the girls' apartment.

The two girls led the way into an upstairs unit. John elbowed Lenny who winked at his buddy and smiled in anticipation of what the night held in store. The dark haired girl indicated that Lenny and John should have a seat on the couch and began lighting candles and sticks of incense.

Once Lenny and John's eyes had grown accustomed to the dark room they began to examine their surroundings and noticed glowing stars and fluorescent crescent moons placed all around the room, on the walls and even attached to the apartment ceiling. There was a Oujie board on the table in front of the couch and Tarot cards on the coffee table, along with several books about the occult. Next to an ashtray on the same table was a bong—a pipe used for smoking marijuana and hashish—shaped like a human skull. Above the mantle, Lenny was startled to see a painting of a classic Satan, complete with horns and gleaming red eyes.

The two guys looked at one another quizzically and Lenny raised one eyebrow. John just shrugged, as if to say, "So what?"

Before they could spend too much time contemplating their unusual surroundings, the pale-skinned blonde emerged from the kitchen carrying an ashtray with four purple glasses. She placed the tray on the table next to the Oujie board and sat down beside John. Her friend came over and sat beside Lenny. Handing him one of the drinks, she picked one up for herself and said, "Drink up."

Lenny couldn't identify the sweet tasting fluid. It wasn't like anything he'd ever had before. At the brunette's insistence, however, he drank it down quickly. As soon as he did his head started spinning. The candles in the room seemed to grow brighter and their flames seemed to leave the individual candles and float around the room in midair. The stars and crescent moons seemed to rotate around the room, slowly at first, and then faster and faster. Lenny could tell by the look on John's face that the strange concoction was having a strange effect on his friend as well.

The two girls downed their drinks as well and then stood up. "We're going to get a little more comfortable," she said, then, taking her friend by the hand, led her off into what Lenny assumed was the bedroom. Lenny just sat on the couch, wondering what had been in the drink to do such strange things to his mind. John stood up and began wandering around the room.

After what seemed like only a few seconds the girls came back into the room. Each was dressed in black and each was carrying a candlestick with a black candle. The flames of the candles illuminated the girls' faces and Lenny was shocked to see that they had added dark black mascara and deep red lipstick.

The blonde asked John to accompany her into the kitchen and help prepare some more drinks. The brunette walked over and took Lenny's hand, pulling him up off the couch. "Did you like your drink?" she asked him in a low, sultry voice.

"It was different," Lenny managed to say.

"Let's play a little game," she said to him. "There was a little something special in your drink."

"Yeah," Lenny readily agreed. "I thought there might have been."

The girl smiled at his remark. "It won't hurt you," she assured him. "In fact, it will help you. It will help you get in touch with your true inner being.

"Sit down here at the desk," she instructed, indicating a small table which held only a candle and a manual typewriter with a fresh piece of plain white paper in the carriage. "We're going back in the bedroom and light some candles. While we're gone I want you to just start striking the keys and type whatever thoughts pop into your mind. When you finish, we'll take you back and show you what's on our minds."

John had returned from the kitchen by now, carrying two more drinks. His friend left the room with the brunette. John placed one of the drinks on the table beside Lenny and walked over to a small bookcase in the corner of the room and began to examine a large leather scrapbook that was on one of the shelves.

Lenny took a swig of his new drink and started typing mindlessly. He seemed to be in a trance as his fingers kept striking the keys. Suddenly John shouted, "Holy cow! Lenny, look at this! We've got to get out of here!"

Lenny turned to see what had startled his friend, who was rushing toward him, carrying the heavy scrapbook. "Look at this stuff!" John shouted.

Lenny was shocked as he looked down at the album. It was a book of witchcraft and black magic and both Lenny and John gasped at the graphic pictures, some of which showed ritualistic sacrifices.

"We've got to get out of here!" John insisted, but Lenny just sat at the table, as if in a trance.

Alarmed by John's shouting, the two girls raced from the bedroom. The blonde snatched the scrapbook from John's hands and the brunette raced over and ripped the paper from the typewriter. She took one look at the paper and screamed at the top of her voice—a painful, wailing scream, as if she were being tortured.

Lenny, totally unaware of what he had typed, grabbed the paper from her hand and looked at it. He was shocked to see that there on the paper, amidst a bunch of gibberish and garbled words, was the phrase, "My soul is searching for God . . . for the one, true God."

Lenny and John almost knocked one another over trying to scramble out of the candle lit apartment. "Witches!"

they both cried as they stumbled down the stairs and practically dove into John's van.

As John sped away from the frightening scene, Lenny sat in silence, his whole body trembled as he thought of the words he had unknowingly typed out just a few moments earlier. "My soul searches for God . . ."

For the second time that day, tears rolled down his cheeks and images of his grandparents, heads bowed in prayer, ran through his troubled mind.

Chapter Sixteen

"For the wages of sin is death, but the gift of God is eternal life in Christ Jesus our Lord."

Romans 6:23

7he *Blackfoot* caravan was traveling down a Carolina back road early one Sunday morning. They had opened for the Allman Brothers the night before in that groups's hometown, Macon, Georgia. The band had decided, as a group, that they would pack up and head home after their performance and had subsequently taken turns driving through the night.

Lenny had grown more and more morose since the encounter with the witches several weeks earlier. For a while he tried to figure out why he was so depressed all the time. The more he thought about it, the more confused—and the more depressed--he became. After a while he quit thinking about it at all and began pouring himself into the things that he was convinced would bring him happiness—his music and drugs. Of course there was Susan, too, but only during the weeks the group stayed close enough for him to see her. And on the road there were always plenty of women to keep him company in her absence.

Sometimes Lenny felt guilty when he went out with other girls, because he really did care for Susan and wouldn't want to hurt her. On the other hand, when Lenny went out with girls on the road he wasn't in any condition to think clearly about whether his actions were hurting her or not.

John, as usual, was driving the van. Charlie was

right beside him in the front seat, talking to him and trying desperately to keep John awake. Lenny was sprawled across the back seat, sound asleep. Medlocke and Jackson Spires were following along behind in a separate van.

The group had miraculously made it as far as Greensboro, just 25 miles south of their Reidsville home, without crashing either van or getting arrested for their erratic driving which was, this time at least, caused by lack of sleep rather than illicit drugs. The sun was just peeking over the horizon when John pulled into an apartment complex where several of his friends, all of whom were making a career out of college, lived.

"What are you doing, man?" Charlie asked? "Why are you stopping here? Those guys will be sound asleep and we'll be home in thirty minutes."

"I got to go, man," John replied, grinning sheepishly, "and I'd rather go here than at one of those dirty filling stations out on the highway."

"Well, I might as well go, too," Charlie responded. He shouted at Lenny in the back seat, "Stadler. John's stopping to use the john. You need to go?"

Lenny was sound asleep and barely mumbled a response.

John and Charlie just laughed and headed around to the back of the building where, curiously, their friends' kitchen light was on.

Moments later, John rushed out of the apartment and ran full speed toward the parked van. He jerked the door open, reached in, and grabbed Lenny by the shirt collar. "Wake up, Lenny! Wake up! Wake up!" John yelled over and over, violently jarring his friend to consciousness.

Lenny struggled to open his eyes, completely taken aback by John's behavior. As his eyes met John's he saw a look of terror mixed with grief that he had never before seen, in John's eyes or anyone else's.

"John," he asked. "What's wrong? What's going on?"

"What's wrong?" John replied. "She's dead, Lenny."

"Who's dead?" Lenny questioned, completely unable to comprehend what John was trying to tell him. The next words out of John's mouth cut like a knife.

"Susan, Lenny. Susan! Susan is dead! She died last night—of an overdose."

Lenny couldn't even respond. His mind couldn't—or wouldn't—process the terrible news he had just been given. He just sat in the back seat of the van, staring blankly into space. John eventually climbed into the front passenger seat and sat, sobbing quietly, as Charlie drove the thirty miles home. None of the young men had spoken during the thirty minute drive to the small frame house the boys rented from Lenny's family.

The group's other van, which had not taken a pit stop back in Greensboro, was parked in the gravel drive. Their was no sign of life inside the house, which indicted that the other members of the band were already sacked out inside, unaware of the tragic news about Lenny's girlfriend.

"You gonna be okay?" John asked.

Lenny didn't even respond. He just climbed into his new yellow sports car, his only material symbol of his musical success, and drove away.

He really didn't know where he was heading. He drove aimlessly around the familiar streets of his hometown for close to an hour before turning into the driveway of his parents' home. He walked around to the back door and walked wordlessly into the kitchen where his father, already dressed for church, sat reading the Sunday paper. His mother was taking a pan of hot biscuits out of the oven. She took one look at her son and her heart broke.

He looked like a stranger—thin and gaunt and hollow eyed. His long hair was dirty and stringy, his clothes wrinkled and unkempt. She looked at his face, and into his lifeless eyes.

"She's dead, Mom," Lenny said in a quiet voice. "Susan's dead."

Dorothy Stadler didn't say a word. She just walked over and embraced her son. Leonard Stadler, not knowing what to do or say, got up from the table and went to church. When he returned, several hours later, he found Lenny sound asleep, back in his old boyhood bedroom.

Leonard and his wife sat around the kitchen table most of the afternoon while their son slept. They talked about Lenny, voicing aloud for the first time the depth of their concerns about his chosen lifestyle.

Dorothy cooked a big supper that evening, which was

not her custom on Sundays. When it was time to eat, she couldn't bring herself to wake her son who was sleeping so soundly. She and Leonard ate alone and then went to a Sunday night church service, leaving behind a plate heaped high with roast beef, mashed potatoes, and green beans.

When they returned home, Lenny's yellow MGB was not in the driveway and as they entered the house, Dorothy noticed immediately that he hadn't touched the food she had left for him. She sat down at the kitchen table, buried her face in her arms, and began to cry.

Leonard Stadler, for the second time that day, left the house alone. He returned a short time later, along with his father-in-law, Johnny Bullock. The older man walked over to the kitchen table where his daughter still sat, sobbing softly.

He pulled up a straight kitchen chair and sat down beside his daughter, placing a work-callused hand on her shoulder. "Lenny's lost, Dorothy. Satan's got a hold of him and there ain't nothing we can do about it except pray that God will lead him back into the path of the righteous."

Dorothy lifted her tear-stained face and looked into the caring eyes of her father. "I'm scared," she admitted. "I'm scared for Lenny. I'm scared that what happened to his friend will happen to him."

"I'm scared, too," her father admitted. "Not that he'll die," he added, "but that he'll die without Jesus. Eternity is a mighty long time to spend in hell."

The weeks that followed Susan's death were empty ones for Lenny. He immersed himself even deeper into his only means of escape--drugs and music. Not a day passed that he didn't get high. To make matters worse, his mother had abandoned her policy of quietly ignoring his behavior and had started calling him on the phone and even coming by the music store when she knew the band would be practicing. Every time she saw her son she urged, begged and pleaded with him to go by and visit his grandparents. She assured him that his grandmother would cook him his favorite meal--just like the old days. Lenny finally agreed to show up the next Saturday he was in town which, as fate would have it, was the very next week.

As soon as Lenny drove into the driveway he wished he hadn't come. "I've been set up," he thought to himself. Things got worse when he walked into the house and saw the large family Bible on the living room coffee table, opened no doubt to a passage chosen especially for Lenny's benefit. He felt self-conscious as he took a seat on the edge of the couch, his gaze purposely avoiding the gold-edged pages of the large, leather bound book on the table in front of him.

His grandfather joined him on the couch, having to make a concerted effort to avoid commenting on his grandson's appearance. "Do you ever read the Bible these days?" he asked, already knowing the answer.

"No, Pa," Lenny answered defensively. "You know I don't."

"Well you ought to read the red words," his grandfather responded, without a trace of judgment in his voice. "It's all important, but them red words—those are the ones Jesus said. Read the red words, son, if you don't read anything else."

Lenny was about to retort angrily that he didn't care what Jesus said, but before he could his grandmother called out that lunch was ready.

As Lenny took his place at the kitchen table he was momentarily glad he came, even if it did mean listening to a lecture on Christianity. The table was overflowing with platters and bowls of fresh vegetables, fried chicken, gravy and homemade biscuits.

Lenny's resentment returned, however, as his grandfather offered up an extra-long prayer, full of references to salvation for the lost which Lenny knew were for his benefit. Finally his grandfather added an "amen" to his prayer which was echoed by his grandmother. No sooner had Lenny finished serving his plate than his grandfather started in on him.

"Lenny," he started. "I want you to hear me out. I know you don't want to hear what I have to say, but you need to.

"Look at you," he continued. "Your hair is so long it was touching the table when you bowed your head for grace. Your mama pretends she doesn't know what goes on when you're out on the road with that band, but she does—and it's about to worry her to death."

Lenny started to speak, but his grandfather held up

his hand to stop him.

"Wait, Lenny. Hear me out," the elderly man insisted. "Your family loves you, Lenny. We all love you very much and we are praying for you. You need Christ in your life. Satan has a hold of you and he's trying to destroy your life. The road you are traveling leads to nowhere. It's a dead-end. We don't want you to end up like . . ."

Lenny stood up, stopping his grandfather in mid-sentence. He was numb and angry at the same time. He knew that every word his grandfather was saying was true, but he didn't want to hear any of it. He also knew that the conversation was about to lead to Susan and the final destination of her soul. It was a subject that kept Lenny awake at night when he allowed himself to think about it, and he wasn't about to let his grandfather give voice to his own doubts and fears.

Not knowing what to say, Lenny startled his grandparents by saying nothing. He just pounded his fist on the dining table, jarring the dishes and knocking over his glass of iced tea. He turned from the table, knocking over his chair in the process, and headed for the back door. He walked out of the house without a word, slamming the door so hard behind him that it sprang the hinges, very nearly causing the door to fall off.

As he got into his yellow sports car his grandfather rushed out behind him, determined to get in one last word. "I don't know what it's going to take, Lenny, but somehow God is going to wake you up! Someday God is going to answer our prayers for you."

Lenny refused to look at his grandfather or acknowledge his words. He quickly backed out of the driveway and burned rubber as he sped away. As he drove down the road he quickly lit a marijuana cigarette and took several quick puffs. He smoked the whole thing down to the nub, but couldn't reach his accustomed high.

His grandfather's words kept echoing in his ears. "God is going to wake you up, Lenny. Somehow God is going to wake you up!"

Chapter Seventeen

"Then I looked on all the works that my hands had done and on the labor in which I had toiled; and indeed all was vanity and grasping for the wind."

Ecclesiastes 2:11

*I*n the weeks after the confrontation with his grandfather, Lenny retreated further and further into the shell he was determined to create around himself. He was convinced that if he could maintain that shell, which was perhaps more like a cocoon, he could insulate himself from the outside forces that he was convinced were making his life so painful and meaningless.

Lenny tried his best to lose himself in his own distorted world of drugs and alcohol, hard rock music and pleasures of the flesh. *Blackfoot* was becoming more widely known and the members of the band were convinced that they were on the verge of scoring a big recording contract— a contract that would put them over the top and move them up to the highest level of the musical food chain. Lenny went through the motions of being an up-and-coming bass guitarist with an up-and-coming Southern rock band. He and the band kept a grueling schedule, traveling the Eastern seaboard, playing in a different town almost every night, and after almost every concert indulging in wild parties and the sordid behavior that went with them.

As the band became more popular the parties became bigger, the drugs more plentiful, the girls wilder and more beautiful. Lenny was living what some would call the good life. He was making—and spending—more money than he had ever imagined, and yet was more miserable than he had ever been. Lenny told himself that he was simply mourning the loss of Susan, and he did have a hard time coming to grips with her death—at least when he was sober enough to think about Susan at all. He avoided spending time with his parents and absolutely refused to see his grandfather.

His friends were so caught up in their own lives that they didn't even notice Lenny's morose behavior. They simply played rock music and partied on.

It was a typical Friday night on the road. The concert had gone well and the post-concert party was going even better. There was booze everywhere and drugs were as plentiful as penny candy. Beautiful girls were everywhere and Lenny was surveying the room, trying to decide which lovely lady he would bless with his company that particular evening.

Suddenly, without warning, a sharp pain cut through Lenny's chest like a knife. He screamed out in pain, grabbed his chest, and dropped to the floor. As Lenny lay on the floor, moaning loudly, dozens of people gathered around him, staring curiously at the long-haired young man who was writhing in pain.

"That cat must have gotten some bad stuff," one person muttered.

"Yeah," another agreed, adding "or too much of some real good stuff."

Most of the people in the room were so wasted that

they couldn't really comprehend what was happening and just stood in the growing circle, staring at Lenny and laughing at the comments being made. Charlie was the first of Lenny's friends to realize what was happening. He pushed his way through the crowd and knelt at Lenny's side.

"Call the paramedics!" he shouted.

"What's wrong?" John asked, as he pushed through the crowd and joined Charlie at Lenny's side.

"I don't know man," Charlie responded. "He must have overdosed. I don't even know what he was using, but he needs help."

By this time the pain had begun to subside and Lenny motioned for John and Charlie to wait. "Don't call anybody," he finally managed to get out, speaking through deep painful breaths. "It's not drugs," he insisted. "Don't call anybody. Help me get somewhere to lay down."

Charlie and John helped Lenny to his feet and led him to one of the bedrooms in the back of the house.

"What's going on man?" Charlie kept asking.

Lenny only wished he could tell him. All he knew was that one minute he was eyeballing a group of beautiful women and the next minute he was stricken with the most incredible pain he had ever experienced.

"I guess life on the road is catching up with me," Lenny offered by way of explanation. "Too many late nights and wild parties, I guess. Just let me sleep it off here tonight and then maybe I will be all better by tomorrow."

"Yeah," Charlie agreed. "Maybe so."

"We can all crash here tonight," John offered. "We'll stay here and then hit the road in the morning."

As the two guys made their way toward the bedroom door, John turned out the light and closed the door behind him, leaving Lenny to lie awake in the darkness and wonder what in the world was happening to him.

The next day, as the band was traveling down yet another Southern highway to play yet another concert date in yet another city, the pain hit Lenny again. Just like the night before, it came from out of nowhere and struck without warning. John, who was driving, pulled over on the side of the road and watched helplessly as his buddy clutched his chest and grimaced, biting his lower lip to keep from crying out in pain.

Again, Lenny had no explanation for what was happening to him. Beads of sweat broke out on his forehead as he curled his knees up under himself, trying desperately to find a position that would bring some relief from the excruciating pain. Just as it had the night before, the pain gradually subsided, leaving Lenny limp and breathless—and scared.

Later that night, as the band was backstage about to perform, the pain struck a third time. This attack was even more severe than the previous two, and the duration was even longer. When the pain had mercifully subsided, Lenny looked around at the circle of faces staring curiously at their stricken friend.

"The pain gone?" Medlocke finally asked.

"Yeah," Lenny answered. "It's all gone for now."

"Good," Medlocke responded. "Let's go out and play some music. There's a good crowd out there."

Later that night, as the band was loading their equipment into the back of their old panel truck, Lenny approached John, who had started out as little more than a glorified groupie, but was now *Blackfoot's* very capable road manager.

"When's our next date?" he asked his longtime pal.

"Not until next Friday," John answered. "In Greensboro."

"Good," Lenny answered. "Do you mind skipping the party tonight?"

'No," John said. "I don't mind. "Where do you want to go?"

"I need to go home," Lenny responded.

He had no idea how prophetic those words would turn out to be.

Lenny felt like a small child as he and his mother walked into the small but comfortable waiting room of his family doctor in Reidsville. He had insisted that Dorothy Stadler did not need to accompany him for his checkup, but he was secretly glad that she came with him anyway. Even though he would never admit it, Lenny was scared. It had been five days since the mysterious pain had first struck so unexpectedly. Since then the spells had become more frequent and each was more severe than the last.

Lenny had made sure that he didn't ingest anything that might be contributing to the mysterious pains, not even a beer or a cigarette, and he had slept almost round the clock since arriving back in Reidsville. Still, the pains continued to strike without warning.

Lenny's family doctor looked at him disapprovingly as the young nurse escorted him into the examination room. It wasn't Lenny's long hair or mustache that bothered him. He had been around long enough to see all sorts of styles and fads come and go. What bothered him was the fact that this patient, whom he had known and cared for most of his life, looked so unhealthy. Always thin, Lenny was now emaciated and his eyes were hollow with deep black circles underneath. It was obvious to the experienced physician that the young man he was about to examine had been abusing his body severely.

He was determined, however, to refrain from being judgmental and he made small talk with Lenny about his career and his shiny new sports car as he had him climb up on the hard examination table and take off his shirt.

Lenny watched intently as the doctor listened to his chest with a stethoscope and questioned him about the nature of his problems. He thought he detected concern in the doctor's eyes as the older man felt and prodded the patient's chest and abdomen. After almost twenty minutes of this pushing, prodding, and listening, the doctor handed

Lenny a written order for a set of x-rays at the local hospital.

Lenny became alarmed when the doctor instructed him to wait for the x-rays and to bring them right back to the office. He became even more concerned when, trying to make a joke, Lenny asked, "Think I'll live, Doc?" and the doctor answered:

"Let's see what the x-rays show."

Lenny and his mother were back in the same examination room a few hours later. Lenny once again was sitting on the examination table and his mother on a hard straight chair in the corner of the room. Their family doctor walked into the room, holding the x-rays that Lenny had just had made.

"I'll get right to the point," the doctor said, addressing Dorothy as if Lenny weren't even in the room. "There is a serious problem," the doctor continued. "Lenny needs to see a thorasic surgeon. I made an appointment for tomorrow in Greensboro."

Lenny's mother just sat and stared, trying to digest the doctor's words, but Lenny jumped to his feet. "A thorasic surgeon?" he asked. "Why? For what? What's wrong with me?"

The doctor just looked at Lenny and shook his head. "I'm really not sure how to explain it, Lenny, but you'll find out everything you need to know tomorrow."

"I'm sorry," he added, as he left the room.

Dorothy rushed out of the room in pursuit of the doctor, determined to find out more about her son's condition. The door shut gently behind her and, once again, Lenny was left alone to contemplate this sudden turn in the direction of his life.

Chapter Eighteen

"For my soul is full of troubles,
and my life draws near to the grave."

Psalm 88:3

The Greensboro doctor seemed cold and impersonal to Lenny as he strode into the room, carrying two sets of x-rays—one set that Lenny had brought with him from his family physician in Reidsville, and another set that had been made just a few minutes earlier. For some reason, Lenny had felt very self-conscious about his dress and appearance from the moment he had walked into the plush accommodations of the Greensboro professional building. What seemed cool and appropriate on concert stages and in party rooms seemed very inappropriate here, and Lenny sensed—or imagined—that this unknown doctor looked upon him with disdain because of his appearance and the image he projected.

The doctor placed several of the x-rays on a back-lit viewing screen. "Mr. Stadler," he stated, rather matter-of-factly, Lenny thought, "I have something to show you."

Lenny and his mother watched intently as the surgeon pointed to a shadowy area near what Lenny perceived to be a picture of his heart.

The doctor looked at Lenny over the top of his glasses. "You have a tumor here," he continued, still pointing at the shadowy area. "As you can see, it is very close to your heart. Initial indications are that the tumor is malignant. It needs to come out, but, because of its location . . ." the doctor's voice trailed off temporarily. He took a deep breath and continued.

"It's in a dangerous position," Mr. Stadler. "The operation itself may not be successful."

"What are you saying?" Dorothy Stadler asked. "Are you trying to tell us that the surgery itself could be fatal?"

"Well," the doctor said, "There is maybe a 50-50 chance that we could get all of the tumor without damaging the heart."

Lenny was stunned but managed to ask, "And if I don't have the operation?"

"In that case, Mr. Stadler," the doctor answered, "assuming the tumor is malignant, as I believe it to be, you would have possibly six months."

"Six months?" Lenny asked incredulously. "Six months to live?"

The doctor merely nodded his head.

Lenny's mother started crying uncontrollably. Tears flowed down her face and her shoulders shook.

Lenny, too, was in shock. He sat and played the doctor's words over and over in his mind. "Six months to live. 50-50 chance. Six months to live. 50-50 chance."

Finally Lenny spoke. "You mean it's like flipping a coin?" He asked the doctor. "My life is suddenly like the toss of a coin? Heads I win, tails I lose? Heads I live, tails I die?"

"We will do everything we can, Mr. Stadler." Somehow the doctor's assurances did little to comfort Lenny, or his mother, who was struggling to regain her composure.

"When can you schedule the surgery?" she asked, as soon as she felt able to speak.

"Two weeks," the doctor told her. "We should operate at Duke University Medical Center in two weeks."

Lenny and his mother drove back toward Reidsville in shocked silence. Tears streamed down Lenny's face as he thought about the impending sentence the doctor had pronounced upon him earlier in the day. His mind was like a kaleidoscope, filled with so many images. He saw himself on stage, long hair plastered to his head, sweat streaming down his face, playing his bass guitar like his life depended on it. He saw the faces of so many beautiful young women, many whose name's he had barely known. Images of drugs of every description swirled around in his head. He saw the sweet face of his old high school sweetheart, Gail, and the glowing brown eyes of Susan.

"Susan," he thought to himself. "One minute she was here and the next minute she was just gone. Is that the way I'm going to end up?" he wondered to himself. "Here one minute and then a minute later, just gone?"

For some inexplicable reason, Lenny thought of his grandfather, standing beside his yellow MGB, promising "One day, Lenny, God is going to wake you up."

"Wake me up?" Lenny thought. "Is this the way God works? Is he going to take my life in order to wake me up?"

Lenny desperately wished he could smoke a joint or

take a pill or do something to drive these terrible thoughts from his brain, but he knew that there was no mind-altering chemical that could erase the reality of this moment from his consciousness.

Lenny left his mother in Reidsville to spread the bad news to his disbelieving family and drove alone to Chapel Hill to meet the band and break the news to them. They were almost as astounded as Lenny and his mother had been as Lenny related to them the doctor's prognosis. They just stood in silence, trying to digest the news and not having any idea how to respond.

Finally one of the group reached into a big orange cooler and pulled out a can of cold beer. "Here," he offered. "Drink this. It will make you feel better."

"Yeah," a second band member suggested. "Smoke a joint before you go on. Forget about your problems for a while."

"Yeah," Lenny thought bitterly. "Drink this. Smoke this. Forget about your problems. Easy for them to say," he thought. "They aren't about to die, and I might be."

But not knowing what else to do, he accepted the beer and the joint and started drinking and smoking and trying to forget his problems, at least long enough to perform.

That night's performance was like none other in Lenny's career. He stood in front of the massive wall of amplifiers, giving himself completely to his music. He played as if it would be the last time he ever appeared on stage, and, for all he knew, that might very well be the case.

The band was swarmed under backstage after the concert. All the members of *Blackfoot* knew that Lenny had carried them that night and they swarmed around him after the curtain went down on their performance.

"Man, Stadler, you were cooking tonight," Jackson Spires offered.

"Yeah, Stadler," Medlocke joined in. "What happened," he teased, "You get a glimpse of that hot blonde on the second row or something? Don't worry," he added, "I sent John to invite her backstage. She should be here any minute."

"You want something to drink?" Charlie asked quietly. Lenny looked up at the guitarist and was surprised to see that he held out a glass of water and not a beer.

"Yeah," Lenny said. "Thanks."

"Where's the blonde?" Medlocke shouted out to John, who had just joined the backstage gathering.

"I sent her home," John said. "Different party tonight, gang. Let's get the equipment loaded up. I've got us a corner table reserved at the Waffle House."

The mood became somber as, for the first time, the guys in the band realized that Lenny's condition affected them all, at least for the time being. They did what John said and loaded up their equipment and headed to the nearest Waffle House.

Over a meal of bacon, eggs, toast, grits, hashbrowns,

waffles, and strong black coffee, *Blackfoot* peered over their calendar for the coming weeks. Luckily, they were in a relatively light period in their schedule, having set aside some practice time to prepare new music for a much anticipated recording session the band was convinced was just around the corner. By canceling a couple of local gigs, they could take a three week break, staying in Reidsville until after Lenny's surgery.

Lenny appreciated the fact that the band was willing to cancel their engagements, but had no idea what to say to his friends or his family. After they returned to Reidsville Lenny disappeared from sight. He didn't care what the band thought and didn't worry about his family's feelings, either. He spent his nights sleeping, or mostly lying awake, on a friend's couch in Greensboro. He spent his days driving his car around, trying to make some sense of this catastrophe that had befallen him.

For four days Lenny hid out in Greensboro. He talked to his mother once a day by phone, each time assuring her that everything would be okay, but in his own mind he felt that life was anything but okay. "In fact," he thought, " life is pretty much meaningless." Every day his mother begged him to come home and stay until the day of his surgery arrived. Every day Lenny promised that he would be home soon. Every day Lenny's mother pleaded with him to go by and see his grandfather, or at least call him on the phone. Every day her pleadings were met with silence.

As he drove the familiar roads around Greensboro, or sat in familiar bars, searching for courage in the bottoms of bottles, Lenny reached the conclusion that life had very little to offer him. For so many years all he dreamed about was becoming a big time rock-and-roll musician. He had become a rock-and-roll musician and was certainly on the brink of making the big time.

"But so what?" Lenny had admitted to himself. It had been fun at first and it remained a rush, playing his bass in front of thousands of people and hearing them react to his music, but after a while, every night was like every other night and the crowds and the concerts, no matter how big or how responsive, had left Lenny with a feeling of emptiness. "There has to be more," he thought to himself. "There has to be something that will fill this void and give me the feeling of fulfillment I'm seeking."

He constantly thought of all the ways he had tried to fill that void—getting high on drugs, music, and women. Everything he tried gave him temporary pleasure, but when the pleasure was gone the emptiness returned, and each time the void was deeper and darker.

"And now," Lenny thought to himself, on the morning of the fifth day after his visit to the Greensboro surgeon, "What do I have to look forward to? Six months of pain and torture with my parents watching me waste away? Having some doctor I don't even know cut me open and dying on the operating table. What if I did survive the surgery? What then? How many more concerts? How many more drugs? How many more meaningless days and nights on the road?"

Lenny Stadler had hit rock bottom. Faced with the possibility of death, he could find no promise in life.

Lenny left his friend's house in Greensboro, headed for his hometown of Reidsville, which was thirty miles away. As he drove his yellow sports car at full throttle, not caring if he were stopped for speeding, he tried his best to find one reason to live long enough to go through his scheduled surgery. He drove through downtown Reidsville, slowing down as he passed his father's music store. Painful thoughts flooded his mind as he thought about his father who always supported Lenny, even when the support wasn't warranted.

He thought about the hand crafted guitars his father was famous for building and he thought about the way Leonard Stadler had given money and equipment and a place to live to the members of *Blackfoot* so that he, Lenny, could pursue his dream. Tears rolled down his face as he thought of the day he had quit Elon College. He thought about standing in that same music store, shaking his finger in his father's face.

"Some dream," Lenny thought to himself as he gunned his engine and sped out of town.

Suddenly, Lenny knew exactly where he was going, and what he was going to do. "Life isn't worth living for me," he thought bitterly, "so why keep living? Why live a life of misery? Why wait another week and die on an operating table? I'll end my life today—right now—on my own terms!"

Lenny pushed his car's accelerator to the floor-board with his right foot. The speedometer registered 70, then 80 miles an hour.

"It will be quick and painless," Lenny said aloud. "Which is more than I can say about life," he bitterly thought to himself as he headed toward the stretch of roadway known to many locals as "Dead Man's Curve."

Chapter Nineteen

"For whoever calls on the name of the Lord shall be saved."

Romans 10:13

7he yellow sports car looked strangely out of place, zooming along the rural back roads near Reidsville, North Carolina. This area, in 1973, was more given to pickup trucks than finely-tuned British convertibles. So, too, did the long-haired young man behind the wheel seem a bit incongruous, not that a passing motorists could have caught more than a glimpse of the desperate person behind the wheel. He was driving much too fast.

They couldn't have seen his eyes at all, as they were hidden behind tinted shades. Anyone who might have looked into those eyes would have found them to be blood-shot—and filled with fear; fear and hopelessness. They were the eyes of a dead man. Spiritually dead, at least. In a few moments, if things went according to plan, the body would join the spirit.

Fear and hopelessness had been every bit as instrumental as the yellow MGB in bringing Lenny Stadler to this crossroads in his life.

The speedometer needle soared as he drove the car faster and faster. The tires squealed as he pushed the high-performance engine to its very limits. Faster and faster he drove the machine along the blacktop asphalt that he knew by heart.

He drove the car like there was no tomorrow, and if he followed through with his plan there would be none—literally. Not for him, anyway. Not on this earth. The pain of too many wasted yesterdays and the fear of the unknown made tomorrow too frightening to face.

Pain and fear. Fear and hopelessness. Hopelessness. "Why face tomorrow without hope? Why not end it today?

"Yes," he thought as he gripped the leather covered steering wheel tighter and tighter—pushing the accelerator with even more force. "Why not end it today? Right here. Right now. Death. Death will solve all the problems. When there's nothing to live for, why not choose death? When a life has already been wasted, why prolong it?"

He gunned the engine again, pressing even harder upon the floored accelerator. Just ahead the road would curve sharply. The yellow MGB would not. The end would be swift and painless, at least for the driver.

"I can do it!" he spoke aloud. "I will do it!" he desperately cried, gripping the wheel tighter and trying to push his foot through the very floorboard of his car.

But then Lenny Stadler heard a voice. Above the roar of the engine, the blaring of the radio, and the desperation in his own soul, Lenny heard an inner voice. A peaceful voice. A voice completely without desperation. A voice that spoke as clearly to Lenny as if it came from the empty passenger seat beside him.

"I am the way."

Over and over that simple statement repeated itself

in Lenny's mind.

"I am the way."

The voice grew louder and clearer.

"I am the way, the truth, and the life. No one comes to the Father except through me.

"I am the way. I am the way. I am the way"

"Yes," Lenny thought. Another way. Another way. There must be another way. There is another way!"

Lenny's foot eased off the accelerator of his car. His death grip on the steering wheel loosened. He wasn't aware of it, but tears began to flow from his bloodshot eyes. He steered his car safely through "Deadman's Curve" and brought it to a stop at the first dirt road beyond. And there he sat, his head resting on his car's steering wheel, sobbing—his whole body racked with emotion as a flood of memories washed over him. Precious memories. Memories that had saved his life without his even knowing it. Memories that would form the foundation of a life more rich and full than he could have possibly imagined.

Lenny didn't know how long he stayed on the side of the road, his head buried in his arms. Finally he wiped his eyes and turned the car around. For the first time in a long time he knew exactly where he was going. He didn't know what kind of reception he would get when he got there and he didn't know what he would say, but he knew where he was going.

"I'll go see Pa," he said aloud. "Pa will help me find my way."

As Lenny drove back toward his grandparents' house he could see his life more clearly than he ever had before. For the first time, he realized that his life had become a spiritual battlefield for the forces of good versus the forces of evil. Evil had almost won, but Lenny finally realized that good could prevail and he intended to do everything in his power to cast the deciding vote on behalf of good, with his grandfather's help.

Something seemed very strange to Lenny as he parked his car and walked around to his grandparents' back door. Usually Lenny's grandmother walked out into the yard to welcome him at the sound of his approach, but now, when he wanted so desperately to see and embrace both of his grandparents, there was no one in sight and the house was unusually quiet.

Lenny took a deep breath and let himself in the back door. "I am the way, the truth, and the life." The small inner voice continued to whisper the message of hope and life in Lenny's mind.

Once inside, Lenny didn't call out as he usually would have, but instead walked quietly through the house. As he turned the corner from the hallway into the living room he was startled to find his grandparents sitting side by side on the sofa, their heads buried in their hands, praying aloud.

"Dear God," his grandfather was praying aloud, "Please help Lenny find his way back to you. Please, dear Lord," Johnny Bullock pleaded, "Please help Lenny find his way back to you."

Lenny's heart melted as he heard this good and gentle man pray this simple prayer. For perhaps the very first time in his life, Lenny realized that he was a child of God. He dropped to his knees in the doorway of the room, tasting the salty moisture of the tears that were streaming down his face.

"Is there still, time, Pa?" he wailed. "Is there still time for me? Can God still help me? Will God hear my prayer?"

His grandfather lifted his eyes and gazed into those of his grandson. Later, Lenny would realize that there had not been one glimmer of surprise in his grandfather's eyes. He had prayed unceasingly for years that his grandson's heart would be touched, and he never doubted for one moment that his prayers would be answered.

He got up off the couch and walked across the room. Kneeling beside his grandson, he draped his arm around his shoulders. His blue eyes were wet with tears of joy. "Yes, son," he stated with assurance, "God is always ready to hear your prayer and accept you just as you are."

"What do I have to do?" Lenny pleaded.

"Do you really want Jesus in your life, Lenny?" his grandfather asked.

"Oh, yes," Lenny responded. "I've wanted him and needed him for a long time. I have felt the hunger and thirst in my soul, but I've been running and hiding for so long, Pa."

"If you want to accept Jesus Christ as the Lord and

Savior of your life, all you have to do is call out on his name," Lenny's grandfather said.

He took Lenny's hand in his own and began to pray aloud, "Dear God, I rejoice this day that you have answered my prayers. Thank you for your amazing grace which alone can save us from our sins."

Finally, Lenny prayed. "Lord Jesus," he said earnestly, eyes looking toward the ceiling of his grandparents' living room. "If you are really real; if you really are who you say you are; I need you in my life."

The words were spoken simply and quietly, but a more sincere prayer had never been offered. Suddenly, a miraculous feeling of peace and joy flooded Lenny's soul as he and his grandfather were joined by his grandmother who knelt beside them.

The trio was still kneeling in prayer when Lenny's parents walked into the room a few moments later. "We are sorry we are late for dinner, but we were busy at the music store," Dorothy offered as way of explanation for their being late.

Lenny looked up at his parents. "It's going to be okay, Mom," he assured his mother. "Whatever happens at that hospital next week, it's going to be okay. I'm ready to face it. I've found the Lord," he told his mother quietly. Then, thinking about his wild drive toward deadman's curve added, "and the Lord has found me."

Though they could hardly believe it, Lenny's mother and father joined in the rejoicing and celebration. His grandmother prepared dinner, and it was truly a sacred meal for the Stadler family.

And that night, on the eve of his twenty-first birthday, Lenny slept soundly, for his heart had been strangely warmed, his soul was finally at peace, and a grandfather's prayer had been answered.

Chapter Twenty

"And he arose and came to his father . . . his father saw him and had compassion . . . And the son said to him, 'Father, I have sinned against heaven and in your sight, and am no longer worthy to be called your son.'"

Luke 15:20-21

*L*enny Stadler's mother was by his bedside in the hospital room at Duke University Medical Center where he awaited surgery. The past five days had been nothing short of miraculous. Even in the face of uncertainty presented by the life-threatening operation he was about to endure, Lenny had found God's peace in his heart. It seemed to him that he had finally found that slippery, elusive, unattainable spirit of happiness for which he had been so desperately searching.

As Lenny looked into the concerned face of his mother, he tried to calm her nerves. He thought back to the previous day when he had walked through the doors of the hospital amid the stares of the doctors and nurses and other hospital personnel who couldn't help but stare at the long-haired young man who held a suitcase in one hand and a Bible in the other.

Lenny had spent every moment possible during the previous week reading the Bible that his grandfather had given him. "Start out reading the red words," Johnny Bullock had reminded him. "Those are the ones Jesus actually spoke."

"I know, Pa." Lenny had laughed as he answered his grandfather, but this time it was a laugh of joy and understanding without a trace of mockery.

And Lenny read the red words, finding comfort in the promises of the Savior he had waited so long to claim as his own. When he wasn't reading the Bible he was talking to his grandfather, discussing the verses he had read and asking him to explain some of the passages that Lenny couldn't quite seem to comprehend.

His mother's voice interrupted those thoughts of grandpa. "Is there anything I can get for you, Lenny?" she had apparently asked him while he was deep in his own thoughts.

"Yeah, Mom," he teased. "I'll have a cheeseburger, an order of fries, and a chocolate milkshake."

Dorothy Stadler laughed at her son's joke. "I wish I could help you out there, but I can't. How about some ice chips instead?" she offered with a smile.

"I think I'll wait for something better," Lenny responded.

"Say, Mom," he said, in a more serious tone. "I want you to know something."

"What's that, Hun?" she asked.

"I just want you to know that I had a little talk with the Lord yesterday when we checked in. I told him that if I didn't leave this hospital alive, that it was okay. I have given my life to Him and I know that I will be with Him forever. I will be with the Lord forver. No matter what."

"Oh, Lenny," his mother interrupted. "Let's don't think about that."

"Wait, Mom," Lenny said, holding up the finger of

one hand to stop her from speaking. "Let me finish."

"Go ahead," Dorothy told him.

"I also told the Lord that if I did come out of this hospital that I was giving my life to Him and He could use me for whatever purpose He chooses. I meant it, too," Lenny added with conviction.

Lenny's mother went back to the hotel in Durham with a burdened mother's heart. With his mother gone, Lenny opened up his Bible and began to read.

After a while, six doctors, led by Lenny's surgeon, walked into the room and stood around his bed. All had very somber faces.

"Mr. Stadler," he began, "We have a situation that we can't explain because we don't quite understand it ourselves."

Lenny didn't offer any comment, so the doctor continued. "As you recall, we studied the x-rays you brought which were taken in Greensboro a few weeks ago. We even studied x-rays that were taken when you were ten years old. Even at that young age we could see the evidence of the tumor we intended to remove."

"You intended to remove?" Lenny asked, picking up on the surgeon's curious choice of words.

"Yes," the doctor said. "You see, that's the problem. The x-rays we took this morning indicate no abnormality at all. In other words, the tumor is gone."

"Gone?" Lenny parroted.

"Yes. It's just not there. There is no longer a tumor

at all and we don't understand it. There's just nothing in any of our medical books to explain what might have happened."

With tears running down his face, Lenny lifted his Bible. "Doc," he said jubilantly, holding the Bible aloft, "Y'all obviously haven't been reading the right book!"

"At any rate," the doctor continued, "We'd still like to do surgery to try and learn what happened, but since the surgery will now be exploratory in nature, we need for you to sign new consent forms."

"Let me get this straight," Lenny said to the doctor. "There was a tumor but now there isn't a tumor—and you want to cut my chest open anyway and try to find out what happened to the tumor."

"That's just about right," the doctor agreed.

"Can I make one phone call?" Lenny asked.

"Certainly," the doctor said.

Lenny picked up the phone beside his bed and called his grandfather. He excitedly shared the news the doctor had shared with him.

Johnny Bullock was elated at the news, but not surprised. "Son," he said to Lenny, "We've had every church in Rockingham County praying for you. I never doubted the Lord would answer our prayers. Don't let those doctors put a hand on you. I'll be there to get you in an hour."

"You don't need to do that," Lenny told his grandfather. "Mom is at the hotel. She can bring me home."

"Lenny," his grandfather said firmly. "I said I was

coming up there, and I'm coming up there. It will take me about an hour. Tell your mama not to sign anything and get your bags packed. I'm taking you home."

"Yes sir," Lenny said, before placing the phone's receiver back in the cradle.

True to his word, sixty-five minutes later Johnny Bullock walked into Lenny's hospital room, having come to take his grandson home.

As they walked down the hall together toward the medical center's front door, Lenny put his arm around his grandfather's shoulder. "Pa," he said to him. "I think I just got that wake up call that you promised I would get."

"I 'spect you did at that," his grandfather agreed. "And Lenny," he added, "when you get a calling from God, you'd best answer it."

Lenny didn't respond, but he also couldn't forget his grandfather's words.

It was a glorious ride back to Reidsville for Lenny and his grandfather. "Pa, please tell me everything about Jesus," Lenny asked. As his mother followed along in the car behind, Lenny and his grandfather were being blessed by the presence of God as they talked about Jesus and cried tears of joy.

Finally, Johnny Bullock pulled into the parking lot at Stadler Music. Waiting in the parking lot were some of the guys in *Blackfoot*. Johnny looked at his grandson and said, "Son, you go on in the music store and make amends with your dad. He really does love you."

As Lenny got out of the car, one of the musicians walked up to him and said, "Man, we heard they didn't have to operate. That's great news. Now we can get back out on the road and talk to some of those record companies that are interested in us."

Lenny just looked down quietly and said, "Let's talk about it later. Right now I need to see Dad in private."

Leonard Stadler met his son at the front door of the music store with a big hug. With tears streaming down his face he looked at Lenny and said, "Welcome home, boy! Welcome home!"

The long hair was no longer an issue and perhaps not even noticed by Leonard. Father and son were now truly together--for the first time in a long time.

Some of the guys in the band walked into the music store and were happy to see Lenny back home again. John walked over, hugged Lenny, and said, "Man, it's so good to have you back. And we've got some good news for you. A big record company is interested in us and they want to talk to us about signing a five-year contract--two albums a year with concert promotional tours. They will even offer us a signing bonus. They are going to meet us in Charleston in three weeks."

"It's big time," Jackson Spires screamed, picking up a drumstick off the counter and playing a drum roll on the nearest object, which happened to be John's back.

Lenny was absolutely dumbfounded. A dream that had driven him for so long was now about to come true.

Yet, he had made a vow to make Jesus Christ the center of his life, and he believed in his heart that God had spared him for a special purpose. Nonetheless, the guys in the band were all such close friends and he loved making music with them. After all, they had all shared in this dream together for a long time.

Thoughts of life on the road flew through Lenny's mind. In his heart he knew that it would be tough to really live a Christian life on the road while traveling with *Blackfoot*. He wasn't worried about the guys, but the girls were another matter. Yet Lenny thought that he could pull it off and, in fact, serve as a Christian witness.

"When's the next gig?" he asked John.

"Three nights from now--in Charlotte, with *Uriah Heep* and *The Hollies*, two groups from England."

"We're at the Park Center Auditorium," Jackson shouted.

"And Charlotte is one of our hottest places--the people love us there," Medlocke added.

"We'd better start practicing then," Lenny suggested, opening his guitar case and taking out his favorite bass.

"Now you're talking," John said, and for the next three hours Lenny Stadler and *Blackfoot* played exceptionally loud and exceptionally joyful Southern rock music.

Chapter Twenty One

*"In all your ways acknowledge Him, and
He shall direct your paths."*

Proverbs 3:6

*L*enny Stadler sat alone in one of the vans *Blackfoot* owned. He had driven the van away from the Charleston concert hall where his friends were preparing to perform. He parked along the sea wall, down near the Battery, and watched the waves from the harbor lap against the sea wall as a bright full moon climbed slowly out of the Atlantic ocean.

The last three weeks had been an unbelievable test of will for Lenny. He tried to hang out with his friends and pretend that nothing had changed, but of course, everything had changed. Lenny was a new person, a new creation in Jesus Christ—and he was determined to remain true to his promise to follow Christ.

While his buddies were having their normal raucous time, Lenny sat quietly in the van, reading his Bible and praying quietly for the strength to survive the temptations of life on the road.

Every night he tried to concentrate on just playing his music, telling himself that there was nothing wrong with playing music. But as he looked at the faces of the young people in the crowds, he knew that rock-and-roll was more than just music—it was an image and a lifestyle—an image and a lifestyle that was incompatible with a Christian lifestyle.

Lenny found his mind wandering, even during concerts, to various verses of scripture he had read during the long hours on the road. He knew that by continuing to play in *Blackfoot* that he was walking a dangerous line—a line that that would be far too easy to cross. And even worse, he was in danger of leading impressionable young people down the path of destruction that he had so recently escaped.

After the concerts it was easy for Lenny to walk right past the booze and pills and other drugs. They held no appeal for him whatsoever. The young women were another matter altogether. They threw themselves at Lenny as never before and every night he had to struggle mightily to resist the temptation to enjoy the pleasure of their company.

Although he had endured all these temptations over the past three weeks, not to mention the taunts of his friends who did not even pretend to understand Lenny's newfound devotion to religion, Lenny still felt guilty because of his close association with the behavior that he knew was so wrong.

Now the band was about to play in their biggest concert of the year. Afterward they would seek to sign a contract that would pay them all a tremendous amount of money, not to mention bringing them fame and fortune. It would be the culmination of every dream they had ever had. And the very thought of it was making Lenny physically ill.

With a deep sigh, he put the van in gear and drove back to the concert venue, no closer to a decision than he had been when he drove down to the sea wall to begin with.

All the members of the band were upbeat as they prepared for the night's concert. They were talking excitedly about the big meeting that would take place back at the hotel suite. Important people in the record industry were present for the concert.

Lenny was not taking part in the preconcert festivities, which didn't surprise anyone. He hadn't touched anything since coming home from the hospital. The guys in the band didn't really understand the transformation. They thought it was merely temporary gratitude for having been spared the pain of a serious operation. They had no way of knowing, firsthand, the life transforming power of Jesus Christ.

True to the scriptures he was spending so much time studying, Lenny tried to share his newfound peace with his friends without sounding judgmental. All of his words, however, fell on deaf ears. At best, the band ignored Lenny's comments about the power of God's love. Sometimes they teased, or even ridiculed him. More than once Medlocke had reminded Lenny of the things he had done in the not too distant past. Lenny finally made up his mind to continue studying God's Word and trying to follow Christ's teaching while reserving comment to his peers, so the other band members weren't suspicious that something might be amiss as Lenny prepared for their big night in silence.

The concert itself was one of the worst experiences of Lenny's life. He felt like such a hypocrite, calling himself a Christian and yet playing onstage in what now seemed to him a hostile environment. He couldn't help but wonder what the people in the audience were thinking about the band and about him. He couldn't bring himself to risk leading one more person astray by his actions or his continued association in this lifestyle. Something his grandfather had told him many months earlier rang in his ears.

"If you lay down with enough dogs, Lenny, you are eventually going to get up with fleas."

Lenny had done just that. But now he had been washed whiter than snow by the cleansing blood of Jesus Christ, and he had no intention of trading the peace he had found for fame and fortune. Lenny had followed that road for too long and he knew in his heart that it could only lead to death and destruction. As he continued to go through the motions of playing his bass, he began to hear, even in the midst of the loud concert hall, a quiet voice, whispering to him a verse he had read that very morning from the book of Joshua.

"Choose this day whom you will serve."

"Yes," Lenny thought to himself. "I will choose this very day." Before he had finished the first set of that night's concert he had made up his mind that this would be his last concert with *Blackfoot*. If *Blackfoot* was going to make the big time, they would have to make it without him.

The band wasted no time after the concert in striking their set and loading up their equipment. *Edgar Winter* and *Rare Earth* would follow them to the stage and, normally, the members of the band would have stayed for the rest of the concert and the backstage party. But not tonight. Tonight was their night and they were eager to talk to record producers.

Back at the hotel Lenny got out of the van and told the others that he wanted to run up to his room and change. What he really wanted to do was gather his courage and figure out how to break the news to them that he would be leaving the group. As he walked into the dark hotel room, he flipped on a light and sat down on his bed. Picking up his Bible from the bedside table he opened it, at random, to a passage from I John. "If we say that we have fellowship with Him, yet walk in darkness, we lie and do not practice the truth."

"I won't live a lie," Lenny said out loud, although he was in the room alone. He read the verse again and then repeated, "I won't live a lie."

He walked out of the room and down the hall to the elevator. He got off the elevator and strode purposely down the hall to a suite of rooms.

He entered the room and was met with a round of cheers. "All right!" someone shouted. "Lenny's here. Let's get this show on the road."

Only John was quiet. He knew Lenny better than any of the others and realized from the expression on his face and the look in his eye that all was not well.

"What's wrong, buddy?" John asked.

The room suddenly grew quiet as the others realized

that things were not going as planned.

"I'm sorry, fellas," Lenny said to the group as a whole. "I cannot sign any contract or agreement. In fact, I can no longer be the bass player for *Blackfoot.*"

Everyone started shouting at once.

"What are you talking about?"

"Are you crazy?"

"What's wrong with you, man?"

"Cut the kidding, Stadler. It ain't cool."

"I'm not kidding," Lenny answered. "I've been trying to tell you for the past three weeks. I'm not the same old Lenny. I'm a new person. I have decided to make Jesus Christ the Lord of my life and I can't follow Christ and play in *Blackfoot,* too.

One of the record producers stepped forward and addressed Lenny. "If I'm hearing you correctly," he said, "you are leaving the group?"

"Yes," Lenny said. "I have to. I have no choice."

"Well, I'm very sorry," the producer said, "but we want the whole group, just like it is. If Lenny's not a part of the group we will have no deal."

One of the band members grabbed Lenny's shirt collar. "Did you hear that, Stadler?" he asked roughly. "If you quit the deal is off. Tell him you were just kidding."

Another round of angry shouts followed.

"Yeah, Lenny, Tell him you were just fooling around."

"What's wrong with you, man?"

"Are you crazy?"

"Quit jerking us around."

"I'm sorry," Lenny responded quietly. "I just can't stay here any longer. I really do have to go now. I'm sorry."

Lenny found himself confronted with a sea of angry faces, just inches from his own.

Just as before, they were all talking at once. Then someone threatened, "I'll kill you Stadler. If you cost us a recording contract, it will cost you your life."

Finally, John was able to separate Lenny from the others and hurry him out the door.

Lenny immediately went up to his room and gathered up his things. He knew he'd have to find another ride home to Reidsville. He wasn't going to be welcome in the *Blackfoot* vans.

As he rode back to Reidsville with an acquaintance, he was completely at peace. He knew he had done the right thing. He knew that for the rest of his life he would follow Jesus Christ, wherever that path may lead, without ever looking back.

Chapter Twenty Two

"And I heard the voice of the Lord, saying:
'Whom shall I send, and who will go for us?'
Then I said, 'Here am I! Send me.'"

Isaiah 6:8

7he following weeks and months weren't easy for Lenny Stadler. Even though he had found a perfect peace in his soul, there were still lots of decisions to be made, and he still had to come face to face with his former band mates on an almost daily basis.

For one thing, he had to have a job, so he went to work in his dad's music store. Leonard Stadler had fronted lots and lots of money to Lenny and his friends for amps and guitars and other equipment and now, with the band on hiatus, his prospects for getting paid were not very promising. To his credit, Leonard never pressed the boys for money and, in fact, wound up writing off thousands of dollars worth of charges and rent.

The members of the band decided to stay right there in Reidsville, at least for the time being, which created a lot of friction. In a town that small, there had to be a lot of incidental contact between Lenny and the others. They were not at all eager to forgive and forget. Without a bass player they were in limbo as a band. The guys all took jobs in a nearby cotton mill to make ends meet and every day when they headed into the hot, grimy factory they blamed Lenny for their predicament. There were times that Lenny really did fear there would be physical retribution from the decision he had made.

Lenny spent a lot of his time studying the Bible. He wanted to learn everything he could about God's Word and about God's plan for his life. He was also astute enough to realize that in order to live a Christ-centered life, he would have to surround himself with other Christians. To this end, he started dating a local girl named Janet Paschal, who was, herself, a committed Christian. It was quite an enlightening experience for Lenny and Janet helped him learn an important lesson—that Christians could have a good time, too—without having to resort to mind altering chemicals or other sinful endeavors.

One night Janet invited Lenny to what she described as "her kind of concert." They went to hear a gospel group called *The Sammy Hall Singers.* After the show, Janet, who was never the one to be bashful, pulled Lenny up on stage and introduced him to Sammy Hall, sharing, in the process, Lenny's testimony with Sammy. Sammy was immediately interested in Lenny's story and invited him to come out to his bus and visit.

Lenny and Sammy had a long talk about the Christian faith and serving God through a ministry of music. Before the evening was over, Sammy indicated to Lenny that he might be needing a new bass guitarist in his group. Lenny indicated that he might be interested, and the two agreed to pray about it for a while.

A few weeks later, Sammy called Lenny up and invited him to join the band. Lenny felt that the timing was right and accepted. In a few days he packed up his things and headed to Sevierville, Tennessee. Once again Lenny would be on the road as a musician, but this would be a very different experience from the one that had almost cost him his life.

For almost two years Lenny traveled the country with *The Sammy Hall Singers.* In doing so, he had the opportunity to share his testimony with thousands of young people. Lenny was so fulfilled by watching and leading teenagers to give their lives to Christ. In some small way, he hoped his witness as a Christian musician was helping to make up for having possibly led people astray during his *Blackfoot* days.

Unknown to Lenny, the night before he was to meet his eventual bride, Lenny drove the bus all night to Dallas, Texas. Sammy Hall, the lead singer in the band, had flown in the day before and been met at the airport. Some of the youth picked Sammy up at the DFW airport. Sammy commented to the senior minister's daughter, Shana, "I want you to meet my bass player, Lenny Stadler." The youth crusade was to be held during Easter break week at Tyler Street United Methodist Church.

The next morning, Shana decided that it couldn't hurt to go up to the church sanctuary to have a look at the bass player. Lenny and the band's drummer, Mike Cane, were getting the equipment set up for the evening concert. Shana, who breezed into the sanctuary that morning, intrigued Lenny. She was in blue jeans, a checkered shirt and, of all things, her hair was in a bandana. Lenny was definitely interested but realized right away that she was younger than most of the girls he usually dated.

Since Lenny had been up all night driving the Silver Eagle bus, he hadn't shaved yet. Shana thought he looked pretty rough. He was dressed in a T-shirt and jeans. His hair was really long. Nonetheless, Shana decided to take a chance and agreed to go with him for a pizza after the evening service.

The date for pizza had gone okay so the next afternoon they decided to play tennis. The rest of the week they were together every chance they got, getting to know one another better. When it was time for the band to leave, they were both upset at having to say goodbye. Lenny was really surprised that he wasn't at all ready to get back on the road. Shana wasn't sure exactly what she was feeling. Later she would look back and realize that she was sixteen and falling in love.

Lenny called her about two nights later and the long distance relationship began. Shana's parents were sure it would fizzle out, so did nothing to stop it. After all, Lenny was twenty-two and Shana was sixteen.

As Lenny left Dallas and headed back out on the road he couldn't get Shana off his mind. He met girls—beautiful girls—at every concert stop. But there was just something special about this one. After a couple of days he decided to take a chance. He sent her a letter, care of her father's church. To his delight, when the band got back to Sevierville he had a reply from her waiting in his mailbox.

Lenny immediately sent an even longer letter and, before he realized what had happened, he and Shana found themselves in a long distance relationship consisting of cards and letters and very expensive phone calls.

Lenny knew instinctively that the chemistry was just right between them and he managed to break away from the band's tour schedule to fly to Dallas three times over the next several months. The first time he flew back they had only known each other a couple of months, which didn't prevent Lenny from asking Shana to marry him. Neither did it prevent her from saying yes, thus beginning a two year long-distance courtship.

Shana's father had reservations about his daughter dating a long-haired bass guitarist in a gospel band, but he never said so.

Lenny gave Shana an engagement ring when she was a freshman at Oral Roberts University in Tulsa, Oklahoma.

She told him at the time, "I have just one question."

"What's that?" he answered.

"Do you have any plans to become a preacher?"

"No way!" Lenny responded.

"Good," Shana replied. "Growing up as a minister's daughter is like living in a fish bowl. I am ready for some privacy. We can share Christ with people by being committed lay people. I don't want to spend the rest of my life being observed by church members."

After a two-year, long-distance courtship, Lenny and Shana were married, with Shana's father officiating. In the interim, Lenny had returned to Elon College to seek a college degree. If for no other reason, he wanted to prove to himself, his parents, and his teachers that he was, indeed, capable of finishing what he started. After their marriage, he and Shana moved back to Reidsville and they attended Elon together. His professors were astonished. They couldn't believe that this respectful, intelligent young man was the same person who had scattered his books across the floor and quit school three years earlier. Indeed, he would continue to amaze them by not only graduating, but graduating with honors.

Between classes and a part time job in his father's music store, Lenny also played bass guitar with a local Christian group called *Shekinah*. A big part of *Shekinah's* ministry was an effort to reach kids on the street—kids who would never, ever darken the doors of a church. The band set up a couple of coffee houses and night after night after night Lenny would share his testimony with all who would come to hear. He was always amazed at the impact his story had on those who heard it and he began to realize that everything that had happened to him had happened for a reason.

It wasn't by accident that Lenny Stadler had been given the gift of being able to play a bass guitar. And though he had chosen a temporary path of sinfulness and destruction, it certainly wasn't by accident that he had seen the wickedness of his ways and given his life to Jesus Christ.

During these days back in Reidsville, Lenny spent a lot of time thinking about his grandfather and others who had prayed for his salvation, even when it had looked as if he was not worth salvaging. He often thought about the miraculous healing that had taken place inside his body and the even more miraculous healing that had taken place inside his soul.

He knew that God had spared him for a reason. He also remembered that he had promised God that he would follow wherever the path of righteousness might lead. Throughout his senior year at Elon, Lenny sensed God had a particular calling for his life, but he just couldn't bring himself to accept that call.

Lenny became convinced that God wanted him to enter full-time ministry—as an ordained pastor in the United Methodist Church. He struggled with this call and tried to convince God, and himself, that he could be just as effective and reach just as many people with his coffee house ministry and band, *Shekinah*. In the end, however, Lenny realized that he could no more turn his back on God's call than he could have signed a record contract years earlier.

Lenny and Shana were attending a revival service back in his home church. The preacher was the same pastor who had confirmed Lenny at Woodmont United Methodist Church when he was twelve years old. At the end of the service an invitation was given and Lenny responded without even realizing it. As he walked down the aisle of the church to kneel at the alter in prayer, he said, "Lord, here I am. I don't know just what you want, but here I am."

As he knelt at the alter, he prayed, "Lord, whatever you want to do with my life, here I am."

As soon as he uttered that brief prayer, Lenny experienced a wonderful feeling of reassurance. He knew that he had made the right decision and, once again, he would never look back.

Interlude

"For I know the thoughts that I think toward you,' says the Lord. 'Thoughts of peace and not of evil, to give you a future and a hope.'"

Jeremiah 29:11

*L*enny had never been one for waiting around. Once he made up his mind to do something, he went full speed ahead. Even though it was already late summer, he went ahead and made application to two seminaries for fall semester: Duke Divinity School and Asbury Theological Seminary.

He and Shana decided to drive over to Wilmore, Kentucky to have a look at the Asbury campus. They met with the dean of the seminary who told Lenny that, since he had applied so late, he would have to actually take classes at Lexington Theological Seminary, as the classes at Asbury were filled to capacity.

As they drove back toward North Carolina, Lenny began to have doubts about taking classes in Lexington instead of on the Asbury campus.

When he got home he learned, to his great surprise, that he had been accepted at Duke. The only problem, other than the fact that Lenny felt completely inadequate, academically, to attend Duke, was housing. There was none available at that late date. At least that is what Lenny and Shana thought. Even the dean of students told them that it would take a miracle to find a suitable place to stay so close to the beginning of classes.

Of course, Lenny and miracles were not strangers to one another. The first place he and Shana applied was Duke Manor, an apartment complex less than a mile off campus. Duke Manor was the most convenient and the most preferred of all the apartment complexes in Durham. Lenny was almost embarrassed when he walked into the manager's office and inquired about vacancies.

The manager looked at him incredulously and responded, "You know, we've been booked up for months now, but a couple came in this morning and asked to be released from their lease. I have one apartment open out of three hundred. It's yours if you want it."

The Lord continued to guide the lives of Lenny and Shana Stadler. He blessed them with a baby daughter in 1981. They named her Shalen, using the first three letters of each of their names. She didn't get here the easy way, though. It took a 42 hour labor, a failed delivery, an emergency C-section, and lots and lots of prayers. Mother and baby almost died, according to the attending physician, but God somehow pulled them through.

In 1987, a second child, LenPaul, was born in Asheville, North Carolina. He had the audacity to show up three weeks early, thus earning the nickname "Interstate Baby."

While shopping for some "baby things" in Asheville, Shana realized that it was time to get to the hospital. Lenny jumped on the interstate and headed for Hickory, North

Carolina, an hour-and-a-half away. He was promptly pulled over for speeding by an alert North Carolina State Trooper. When the officer realized what was happening, he radioed for an ambulance. Lenny was scared to death that the first responders wouldn't understand that Shana needed to deliver the baby by Caesarean, and almost caused a riot back at the hospital. Finally, an understanding doctor put his hand on Lenny's shoulder and reminded him that, "God is in control and everything will be fine."

He was, of course, and everything was.

God had great plans for Lenny Stadler's life. He did, indeed, graduate from Duke Divinity School—with honors. In 1985 he finally got inside a classroom at Asbury Theological Seminary, graduating in 1987 with a doctorate degree in Spiritual Formation.

He is now Senior Pastor at Weddington United Methodist Church in Weddington, North Carolina and in 1995 was awarded the prestigious Harry Denman Evangelism Award by the Western North Carolina Annual Conference. In addition to leading one of the largest churches in western North Carolina, he also speaks at revivals and camp meetings all across the South. In fact, Lenny Stadler is convinced that the most remarkable part of his story is just beginning.

Epilogue

*"How then shall they call on Him in whom they have not
believed? And how shall they believe in Him of whom they
have not heard? And how shall they hear without a preacher?
And how shall they preach unless they are sent?"*

Romans 10:14-15

*I*t was a hot August night at Salem Campground, near Covington, Georgia. Camp meeting was in session, just as it had been every summer since 1828. Lenny Stadler was preaching at Salem. It was the third time, in fact, that he had been invited to preach at the historic old camp meeting.

His partner for the week was Marshall Edwards, a local favorite who had actually graduated from nearby Newton County High School, back in the 1950s. Lenny and Marshall seemed to compliment one another beautifully and everyone in attendance each night seemed to be in agreement that the 2001 session was one of the best in recent memory.

Lenny had preached a particularly emotional sermon that night and was completely drained, physically—from the heat, and emotionally—from the sermon and subsequent alter call. He walked up the slight hill from the campground's tabernacle toward the historic old hotel, which was his home for the week, wanting nothing more than a glass of ice water and a chance to relax in his air conditioned room.

A group of ladies were sitting in wooden rocking chairs on the front porch of the hotel, fanning themselves with pasteboard funeral home fans. One of the ladies stopped Lenny and offered him a copy of the local newspaper for that day. "You made the paper, Dr. Stadler," she said to him. "Take this up to your room and read about yourself."

Lenny thanked her and promised to do just that.

After being stopped a half-dozen more times by well wishers wanting to compliment him on his sermon, Lenny finally made it to his room. While he was waiting for the shower to warm up, he thumbed through the newspaper he had been given in search of the story about camp meeting. What he found was a human interest column by a local writer. Lenny Stadler was the subject.

Lenny turned off the water, deciding his shower could wait, sat down on the side of his bed, and read the column. As soon as he had finished he called Shana on his cell phone and excitedly read these words to her:

Former Rocker Now Moves to a Different Beat

He's trim and tanned with an air of youthful stylishness about him. You'd never guess that he is nearly fifty years old. Most fifty-year-olds more closely resemble me— thinning gray hair, a bit of a belly—you know the type. Not this guy. I really don't think you'd peg him as a preacher right off the bat, either—any more than you'd peg him for a hard Southern rocker from the Allman Brothers/Lynyrd Skynyrd era. He's a people person, to be sure—the kind of guy you'd want to play a round of golf with. But I believe he'd strike you as maybe an insurance salesman or a real estate broker, not a preacher.

I suppose he is a salesman, in a way. The truth is, he

once was a hard rocker—a bass guitarist with a group called Blackfoot. They were a big arena group. They toured the country, played before thousands of people, and made vinyl albums. They had roadies and groupies—the whole nine yards. They were big time, you might say.

And make no mistake about it—he is a preacher. A dyed-in-the-wool old time evangelist who knows the power of the Gospel first hand. He is, in fact, so much a preacher that the powers-that-be in Western North Carolina have seen fit to leave him at his Weddington United Methodist Church appointment for 13 years. That's quite a tenure for Methodists who, in the not too distant past, believed that almost all ministers outgrew their usefulness, if not their welcome, after four years at the same church.

His name is Lenny Stadler and he will be telling his remarkable story at Salem Camp Meeting tonight at 8 o'clock. Yeah, I know I already wrote about one Salem preacher this week, but trust me, you'll want to hear Lenny Stadler's story, too.

I won't steal his thunder, but I will whet your appetite with a bit of a preview. You see, this guy was a Methodist all his life, but as a teenager learned to play a bass guitar and fell in love with rock-and-roll music. I mean really in love with it. You've heard the expression "drugs and sex and rock-and-roll?" I don't want to speak for Lenny Stadler, but I'm willing to bet that when he speaks for himself he will tell you that the expression is neither inaccurate nor overblown.

Rock-and-roll music was more appealing to this young man, who was raised about a mile-and-a-half off Tobacco Road, in Reidsville, NC, than college. He left school after a year or so and headed for Jacksonville, Florida. The British music invasion, started by the Beatles, had evolved into a harder form of rock music and was about to be transformed again, into a mystical blues-influenced sound known as Southern rock.

With hair down to his waist, Lenny Stadler formed his own band, Blackfoot. He and his band moved their operation back home to North Carolina and set out to see the world, so to speak. According to his own testimony, which he will be giving tonight, Stadler was letting the good times roll and giving little thought to his Christian up-bringing. "I'd have time for that when I was 90 and too old to have a good time," he recently told me.

God and his grandpa had a little different time-table however. You'll have to come to Salem to hear the whole story, but it's a good one—complete with life sustaining prayer, the miracle healing of a malignant tumor, a young musician pushed to the brink of suicide, and death threats from fellow musicians who were forced to abandon life on the road and go to work in a cotton mill when their bass player found God and quit the band. (I've worked in a cotton mill, by the way, and I can't say that I really blamed the band for being a bit upset.)

As I said, it's truly a remarkable story. Not as remarkable, however, as the person Lenny Stadler has become.

He has been transformed from a shy young man who would cut English class in high school, rather than give an oral report, to one of the most accomplished ministers in the United Methodist Church.

After his Blackfoot experience he toured with a contemporary Christian group, the Sammy Hall Singers. It was while touring with this group that he met Shana, who would would become his wife and, by his own admission, help keep him focused throughout his life. He would go on to graduate from Elon College, Duke Divinity School, and Asbury Theological Seminary.

Lenny Stadler now serves one of the largest churches in North Carolina, travels extensively in an effort to win people to Jesus Christ, and is becoming an accomplished religious author. His first book, "Where Will You Be When You Get Where You're Going?" will soon be followed by a second collection of his sermons, due out this fall.

He has quite a story to tell. You really ought to come to Salem Camp Ground tonight and hear him tell it. You might as well. The Braves' game will still be going strong when you get home, there's nothing else on television except reruns, and I guarantee you that Lenny Stadler's story is more interesting and amazing than anything you can rent at Blockbuster. It has a much better ending, too. Bring the young people with you. Everyone needs to hear this story.

Y'all come. Sure enough. When have I ever steered you wrong?

Did I say he was a preacher? Make no mistake about

it. He has made a preacher.

"Shana," Lenny asked when he had finished reading the article. "Are you thinking what I'm thinking?"

"Well, I don't know, Lenny," she replied. "What are you thinking?"

"Well, you know I wasn't originally supposed to preach at Salem this year. They called me at the beginning of the summer because one of the preachers that was supposed to be here was critically ill."

"I know that," Shana responded. "What are you saying?"

"Shana," Lenny continued, "I think God has put me and this writer together. You know I've wanted to tell the story of my conversion in book form for a long time. I've tried and tried to get it down on paper but I just can't seem to make it readable."

"I know," Shana responded, "but what's your point?"

"This guy that wrote this column. I believe he can write my story. I have met the guy before. He's like me. He is my same age and he's from a small Southern town. We've lived through a lot of the same things. I believe he can get inside my head and put my life down on paper."

"Well, heaven help him," Shana teased, "if the poor thing can get inside your head. Have you asked him about writing your book?"

"Not yet," Lenny said. "I just read the column. But I'll find him tomorrow and see what he thinks. If it's the

Lord's will he will do it, and if he does, I believe we can touch a whole lot of lives."

"God can," Shana reminded him.

God can indeed. Lenny and the writer did, indeed, meet and pray about the project. They eventually decided that God did want them to reach out and try to touch others by telling the story of God's saving power, as demonstrated in the life of one lost young soul who, by the grace of God, made a miraculous transformation from hard rock to the solid rock of Jesus Christ.

". . . and the gates of hell shall not prevail against it."

*P*raying before the Nation

*"If My people who are called by My name will humble them-
selves, and pray and seek My Face, and turn from their wicked
ways, then I will hear from heaven, and will forgive their sin
and heal their land."*

II Chronicles 7:14

*O*n May 14, 2001, just eight short months after our nation had suffered the most horrific attack on American soil since Pearl Harbor, Lenny Stadler took the podium in the United States House of Representatives and prayed the following prayer:

Almighty God, I come to you in the matchless name of Jesus Christ. I give thanks to you for our great nation. I thank you for the vision you gave to our forefathers and the divine plan by which to govern our nation.

I pray for these representatives who have been placed in authority by the people of our nation. May they seek your guidance in all deliberations. May they invoke your wisdom in making the right decisions concerning the social welfare, the economics, and the protection of our nation. I pray that you would instill within this gathered body the desire to be motivated by your just cause rather than by political or partisan causes.

Finally, I pray that you will help all of us realize that the cost of inconvenience is a small price to pay for the safety of our families and our nation in a time of uncertainty.

Amen.

No power on earth could have transformed Lenny Stadler from a lost soul, wandering amid the rubble of the rock-and-roll culture, to a powerful witness for Jesus Christ, respected enough to be asked to present the morning prayer to the Congress of the United States of America.

Thankfully, Lenny Stadler did not have to rely on any power on earth. He was saved by the matchless grace of Jesus Christ and, even today, offers living testimony to the power of the Risen Lord.

May all praise, glory, and honor, be given in His wonderful name.